# The Noel Terry Collection of Furniture and Clocks

Published by York Civic Trust

Sponsored by Christie's

*'One of the best collections of mid-18th century English furniture formed in the last fifty years'*

Christie's

# Contents

Published by York Civic Trust, Fairfax House,
Castlegate, York YO1 1RN
In association with Christie, Manson and Woods Ltd,
8 King Street, London SW1Y 6QT

© Copyright York Civic Trust
First published 1987

Photography by A. C. Cooper, Jim Kershaw
Text by Peter Brown
Design by Nigel Kirby, LSIA
Printed by Maxiprint, York, England

# Foreword

When the Trustees of the Noel G. Terry Charitable Trust decided to give Noel Terry's collection of furniture and clocks to the York Civic Trust, they were in fact fulfilling Noel Terry's often expressed wish.

He had originally desired that the collection should remain at his home, Goddards, and that the house be opened to the public, but he was wise enough not to tie the hands of his Trustees too tightly and he left the decision to them, with the proviso that whatever happened, the collection should stay as an entity in the city of York.

Goddards was a Tudor style house rather incongruously filled with a collection of what is predominantly mid-Georgian mahogany furniture. The smallness of the rooms, distance from the centre of York and the nature of access, were just three of the factors which influenced the Trustees to decide against leaving the collection where it was and when the York Civic Trust broached the idea of restoring Fairfax House in the centre of York as a permanent home for the collection, it offered the best possible solution. The house, which belonged to the York City Council was unquestionably the finest Georgian town house in York with superb plaster work ceilings by the Italian master stuccattore Joseph Cortese and was a natural home for the Collection. Earlier approaches by the Trust to the City Council with the object of buying the house had met with an indeterminate response but this was to change in the light of the Trust's offer and the Council finally agreed to sell the house.

A complete catalogue of the collection was always intended, but only made possible by the splendid offer of major sponsorship from Christie's. Our heartfelt thanks are extended to the staff of Christie's and in particular to Paul Whitfield, Conall Macfarlane, Richard Garnier and Charles Cator for arranging this and for giving so freely of their time and expertise.

Further extremely generous support was offered by the Trustees of the Noel G. Terry Charitable Trust, who kindly agreed to pay for all the photography and design costs. Additional important sponsorship has also been received from the Friends of Fairfax House and from P. B. Curran, our Insurance Brokers.

Christie's have stated that Noel Terry created one of the best private collections of mid-18th century English furniture formed in the last fifty years. No mean praise, when we consider that it was put together during the halcyon years of the great country house sales and also when so many examples of this type of English furniture were being made available for collectors.

Not surprisingly, Noel Terry's 'bible' during his collecting life was the three part *Dictionary of English Furniture* written by P. Macquoid and R. Edwards, published by *Country Life* in 1924-27 and revised in 1954. These and other standard reference books of the day by such authorities as R. W. Symonds and Margaret Jourdain provided a foundation of fact and opinion on which the collection is based. It spans some 200 years of furniture making, starting in the Jacobean period with a buffet formerly in the possession of William Randolph Hearst (p.30) and when viewing the collection as a whole, it can be seen that Noel Terry has created what can only be described as his own personal Dictionary of English Furniture.

The presentation of the collection within Fairfax House has required several compromises in order that the integrity of both be maintained. A 20th century English gentleman's taste does not necessarily coincide with that of the 18th century Viscount for whom the house was built and it is unlikely that the house would have been arranged as we see it today.

Noel Terry bought each piece on its own merit and was not interested in creating or fashioning interiors in the style of the 18th century. The items have therefore been spread throughout the house in a logical manner, so that the vast majority may be enjoyed by all.

All the information provided has been gleaned from many sources and is, to the best of my knowledge, as factual as possible at the present time. More information on the individual pieces and furniture makers in general will probably come to light and perhaps it will be necessary to emulate the Dictionary again by providing a revised edition.

I am extremely grateful to the staff of Christie's and in particular to Charles Cator for help and advice in the preparation of the text, to the Furniture Department at the Victoria and Albert Museum for unrestricted access to their records and to Dr. Geoffrey Beard, Mrs. Helena Hayward, Dr. Gilbert Vincent, Mr. Christopher Gilbert and Dr. J. E. S. Walker for generously sharing their knowledge and understanding of furniture and clocks.

This catalogue is, in itself, a lasting tribute to a remarkable Yorkshireman, whose consuming passion for English furniture and clocks helped him create a collection that rightly takes its place amongst those of the 1st Viscount Leverhulme, Percival Griffiths and the Hirsch's as one of the great collections of the 20th century.

Peter Brown

Noel G. Terry, whose great grandfather founded the Terry confectionery business, was born in York in 1889. With Queen Victoria still on the throne of an England conscious of its greatness and the guardianship of its Empire, it was a confident, self-assured environment for the early life of a young man, educated at Marlborough and destined to govern a large family business.

His leanings were to politics and economics tempered by a passion for music, especially Wagner. It had been a constant source of disappointment to his eldest son, Peter, who was continually deprived of listening to the music of Joe Loss and Harry Roy on the radio, in favour of Tristan and Isolde.

Noel Terry's education at Marlborough stopped at 16 when he went to work for the Midland Bank in Middlesbrough and it was not until 1911, at the age of 22, that he joined the family business in York. Commissioned in the West Yorkshire Regiment at the outbreak of war, and later wounded, in 1916 he married Kathleen Leetham, youngest daughter of Henry Ernest Leetham, an important York industrialist with interests in flour mills and other Yorkshire firms and the creator of an impressive collection of porcelain and jade.

This link with an established collector probably had the greatest effect on a young man keen to make his own mark in the world. Noel Terry enjoyed telling the story of his first purchase, a piece of porcelain which possibly, in his eyes, could have been of the Ming dynasty. The dutiful father-in-law spent some time inspecting and weighing up the piece before pronouncing - "Very nice m'boy - but hardly a collector's piece!". An important lesson, and obviously well learnt when viewing the consistent quality of subsequent acquisitions.

His collecting started in earnest in 1918 with the purchase of a bureau bookcase for the grand sum of £44 and he acquired his first important painting five years later, a still life by R. Steenwyck (1655), for about the same amount.

By this time Noel Terry had risen in the firm to be Joint Managing Director, a post that he held with his half-uncle, Sir Francis Terry. Desiring a suitable residence, he approached the noted York architect Walter Brierley (sometimes described as 'the Lutyens of the North') and asked him to design a new house in York. The result was the creation of Goddards, completed in 1927. It was the last house which Brierley designed and in it he brought together many of the lessons he had learnt over the years, so that it is neither Jacobean, nor Georgian, Queen Anne or Vernacular, but a fusion of all these styles. In the autumn of that year the family moved in and by 1929, following the birth of his third son, Richard, Noel Terry set about furnishing the house.

His tastes were very particular and surprisingly consistent. A family photograph of him playing on the beach with his children, wearing a suit and winged collar is testament to his conservative, traditional attitudes and this is borne out when viewing his collection of furniture. His dislike of gilding and anything too ornate, coupled with a demand for excellent quality was soon understood by several dealers and he limited his purchases to those he knew and trusted.

His local dealer was Charles Thornton, with premises at The Adams House in Petergate, York. Over the years they developed a close personal relationship and the Thorntons regularly visited Goddards on social as well as business occasions. Noel Terry made a practice of never querying the asking price, reasoning that dealers would only add the amount deducted to the next purchase.

The other firm to whom Noel Terry went for most of his pieces was Mallett of London. It is likely that the relationship developed because a director of Mallett at that time was also the director of a machinery firm which made chocolate processing plant and the bond of common interests developed into one of mutual trust. Whatever the reason, there was a positive frenzy of acquisitions in the years leading up to the Second World War, with Mallett supplying 70% of all items. In an effort to preserve his collection at home, Noel Terry instigated a bonus scheme for his staff whereby they earned ten shillings a month extra if nothing was broken or damaged during that period. (No mention has been made, however, of whether the children received extra pocket money for refraining from Battledore or indoor Cricket!)

During the Second World War, far greater matters occupied his attention and in 1944 he was awarded an MBE for his services as Controller of the Royal Observer Corps in York. The death in 1943 of his second son, Kenneth, a pilot in the Royal Air Force, had a devastating effect on the family and friends. One of the fascinating features of many of the pieces in the Terry Collection is the abundance of secret drawers. It was a poignant occasion when we discovered some secret slides in a tallboy, containing old school reports

and letters about Kenneth, together with pencilled messages passed between pilot and navigator during flights.

With the ending of hostilities, collecting resumed unabated, with Charles Thornton and Mallett vying for Noel Terry's custom. Between them, during the ten short years to 1954, they supplied 52 pieces of furniture and clocks. Noel Terry by this time had decided on the period that he preferred and the items purchased dated, almost without exception, from the mid-18th century. A study of the costs at auction for many of the pieces subsequently bought through Mallett at this time, has revealed that the firm were by now acting as agents. Only a modest mark-up was added by way of a fee and it suggests that Noel Terry was developing an increasing confidence in his own connoisseurship.

During the 50's there was a distinct lull in collecting. It was a time when the children were moving away to seek their own paths in life and it was no doubt a time for reflection. A serious illness in 1960 and subsequent operations to his eyes and stomach caused considerable anxiety and for the remaining twenty years of his life he felt that he was living on borrowed time. In fact they proved to be the richest and most rewarding years

of his life. A passionate lover of the City of his birth, he was one of the four Founders, in 1946, of the York Civic Trust which he served as Honorary Treasurer for twenty five years, and in the last ten years of his life showed an ever increasing commitment to the preservation and enhancement of the City. It was this that led to his determination that the collection should remain as an entity for the benefit of the City of York and he therefore set about establishing a Charitable Trust to preserve and endow it. Having recovered his health to some extent, he began collecting again in 1963 with a purchase from Hotspurs of a secretaire cabinet and continued to buy one or two pieces a year right up to 1978. Each item was exceptional, again concentrated around the mid-18th century and very much in the Chippendale tradition, turning what was an outstanding collection of English furniture into one that holds its own with the very best.

Further horological acquisitions were also made during this period with the purchase of a longcase clock by Henry Jones (17) and bracket clocks by Joseph Knibb (16) and George Graham (23), thus bringing his assembly of horological masterpieces to a majestic conclusion, a sample collection virtually unrivalled outside the great public institutions.

Some of the best pieces of furniture in the collection are displayed here in the Saloon at Fairfax House, arranged by necessity, in a 20th century manner, with items placed in the centre of the room and having a range and variety that is unlikely in an 18th century setting. The interior was completed in 1762 for Viscount Fairfax of Gilling Castle, to the designs of John Carr of York and intended as a town residence for the Viscount's only surviving daughter, Anne.

The family moved into York for the winter months and stayed until late April or May. It was generally thought of as the capital city of the North and as such was considered a very fashionable centre for those who did not wish to brave the appalling roads that led to London.

Local craftsmen were used to furnish the house and the Viscount relied on the upholsterer George Reynoldson to provide the soft furnishings. Reynoldson had developed an excellent reputation in Yorkshire and surviving invoices show that he was required by Fairfax to hang the walls of the Saloon with damask and that he supplied one settee with scrolled feet, two armchairs and eight 'mahogone' chairs with fluted feet, all covered in the same material. As an original subscriber to Chippendale's *The Gentlemen and Cabinet-Maker's Director*[6] it is likely that Reynoldson was supplying furniture very much in that tradition and as a consequence it is probable some of the examples on display in the house are similar to those bought by the Viscount.

# Barometers

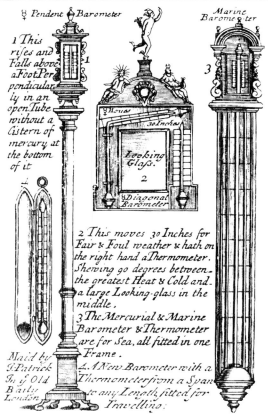

This pamphlet was produced by John Patrick entitled 'A new improvement of the Quicksilver Barometer'. Although undated, it was frequently referred to in John Harris's *Lexicon Technicum*, 1704.

Noel Terry assembled a small but important collection of barometers, which chart, in their own way, the development of the barometer from its first beginnings, through to a time when scientific accuracy was gaining ascendancy over novelty and fashion.

Lack of space prevents this introduction from offering more than a simple résumé of this complex subject and those who wish a greater understanding are referred to Nicholas Goodison, *English Barometers 1680-1860*, 1st edn., 1969 and rev. edn., 1977.

The origins of the mercury barometer can be traced back to 1644 when experiments by Torricelli, a pupil and disciple of Galileo, revealed that the level of a column of mercury in a tube with one sealed end and having an open end inverted into a cistern, would rise or fall subject to variations in climatic conditions.

In England, following the restoration of the monarchy in 1660, renewed scientific interest in this principle was shown by Fellows of the newly formed Royal Society, notably Robert Boyle and Robert Hooke, who sought to promote the development of such a scientific instrument. Leading instrument and clockmakers of the day, particularly John Patrick, Daniel Quare and Thomas Tompion were able to put these theories into practice and eventually housed the mercury column in such attractive cases that the barometer soon became an essential piece of domestic furniture. By 1690 barometers were readily available, found amongst the stock-in-trade of the fashionable suppliers who were eager to attract patronage.

In 1700, John Patrick was advertising a range of barometers for sale at his premises in the *Old Baily, London* and the continuing search for accuracy saw improvements in the arrangement of the mercury. Patrick's advertisement shows, in addition to the straight tube types, a diagonal barometer draped around a mirror with the top of the tube bent over. This causes the mercury to travel a greater distance and magnifies the small variations in level of the liquid.

Further developments involved the use of a syphon tube, where the bottom of the column is bent upwards and left open to the atmosphere. This tube can be used on its own, with the height of the mercury read directly as with the Agar barometer (p.11), or adapted by means of a float, pulley and counterweights to drive a hand round the circular dial of a wheel barometer, often of banjo form.

Straight tube barometers in the latter part of the 18th century invariably used a vernier scale (page 11) to give a more accurate measurement of the mercury level. A means of determining temperature and humidity using sealed alcohol thermometers and 'wild oat' hygrometers (page 12) was also much in evidence.

The primary function of a barometer is to register atmospheric pressure and the fact that 17th century scientists noticed a correlation between changes in the weather and changes in such pressure was very much a secondary issue. These early examples possessed no real degree of accuracy and most barometers were engraved on the face with a series of weather conditions. Whilst these markings were not entirely useless, more information could be gleaned from the instrument by concentrating on the change in level of the mercury from day to day. In addition, the bore of the tube often varied along its length and being made of coarse glass, quickly discoloured, making readings difficult. The mercury was also easily contaminated, would expand with heat and had a capillary attraction for the glass tube that precluded an accurate reading.

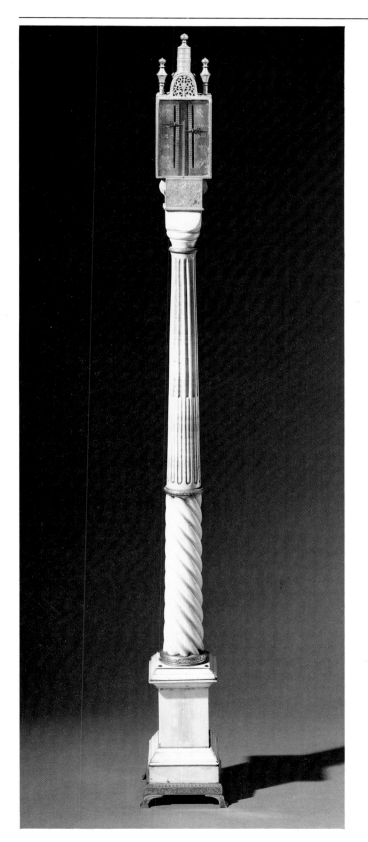

**9. Barometer,** circa 1695
in the manner of Daniel Quare (1649-1724)
Ivory; brass. H.37½ (95)

The piece is constructed in four parts divided by brass collars. A cast brass housing at the top has register plates calibrated from 'Serene and Dry' to 'Rain and Stormy' and two adjustable pointers for recording the level 'yesterday' and today, operated by the two finials that flank a centre finial protecting the extended top of the tube.

The register plate housing of water-gilt brass is engraved with masks and interlaced foliage.

The ivory column is in two parts, with the upper section carved with vertical fluting and reeding, whilst the lower section is spirally twisted. The cistern housing on which it stands has an unusual brass base with bracket feet and may in fact be a later addition, fitted when the original cistern was replaced with the present leather base one.

To the rear, there is a bracket that allows the barometer to be hung on the wall.

PROV: Mallett, 1948

# George Hallifax

**10.   Barometer,** circa 1755
George Hallifax, Doncaster (1725-1811)
Walnut; pine; brass. H.47 (120)

A syphon tube wheel barometer of distinctive shape based on the form of a longcase clock and exhibiting an arched dial set below a caddy top. The register ring is in the form of a silvered chapter ring and the signature disc is surrounded by gilt brass spandrels with the central brass plate engraved in representation of the four elements.

On the trunk, there is a separate recording dial engraved with the same divisions as above, decorated at its centre with an inlaid six pointed star motif, as favoured by the Hallifax family. Confusion is reduced by separating the recorded reading from the current reading shown on the upper dial.

George was the fourth son of John Hallifax of Barnsley, an important provincial clockmaker whose own documented barometers are strikingly similar to this piece. John Hallifax died in 1750 and it may well be that George used up some of his father's stock, despite the fact that his other brother Joseph alone succeeded to their father's business.

PROV: V, 1942 (identity unknown).

**11. Barometer,** circa 1785
John Agar, Castlegate, York (1730-1815)
Mahogany; pine; brass. H.42 (107)

The syphon tube mercury column is housed in a pendant frame and a fluted cover is fitted on the pierced base to protect the bulb, whilst the top of the column has been secured within an acorn finial. A silvered brass plate is set into the frame and on one side registers Summer and Winter variations in the weather, whilst a vernier scale is engraved on the other.

From about 1770 onwards it became common practice for this type of vernier scale to be fitted on household barometers. Formerly it was quite easy to read the height of the mercury column to an accuracy of 0.1 inch, but the introduction of the vernier scale allowed an increase in accuracy to ± 0.01 inch.

Confusion was still possible however due to the capillary attraction of the glass on the mercury and resultant attraction or repulsion whether the column was falling or rising.

PROV: Y. Lloyd-Greame, Esq., Sewerby House, Bridlington. Sold by Anderson & Garland, July 18, 1934, lot 651.
Charles Thornton of York, 1945.

NOTE: B.Loomes, *Yorkshire Clockmakers,* 1985, p.37, cites by the same, 'A longcase clock signed *Jno. Agar-Fulford* and a silver pair-cased watch with a London Hallmark of 1772, no.355, in the British Museum, London'. Registration no. M.&L.A., C.A.I.-353, formerly in the Ilbert collection and acquired by the Museum in 1968.

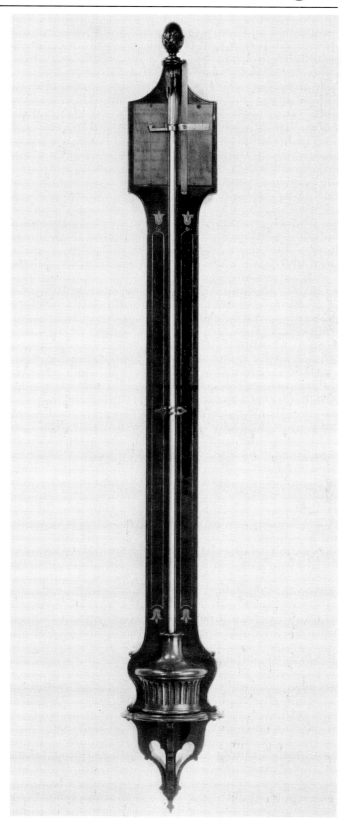

# Polti

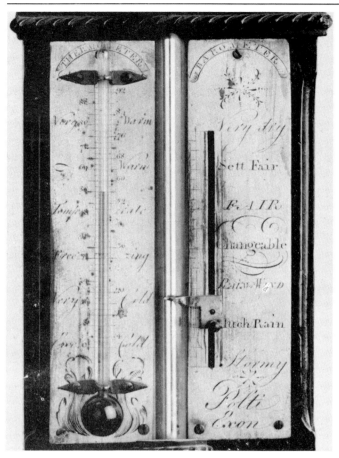

**12.   Barometer,** circa 1790
Charles Polti, Exeter (d.1792)
Mahogany; brass. H.41½ (106)

The cistern tube is supported in a frame of mahogany and is set in a boxwood cistern which has a leather base and screw mechanism for adjustment. The cistern is protected by a cover of pineapple shape, carved with flowers and foliage, whilst the tube is shielded by a length of carved moulding.

At the top a pointer and scale records the mercury level, and a small alcohol thermometer is calibrated in degrees fahrenheit.

Also set below the pedimented top is a hygrometer, intended to register the humidity of the air. An engraved dial shows whether the atmosphere is moist or dry by means of a pointer attached to the beard of a wild oat which unwinds when moistened.

NOTE: C. N. Ponsford, *Time in Exeter,* 1984, p.178 cites from the *Flying Post,* June, 1792 'Monday died suddenly, Mr. Polti, weather glass maker, of this city: he was a very honest man, and an ingenious mechanic.'

# Early English Clocks

The object of this brief introduction is to place Noel Terry's collection of clocks within the historical development of horology and those who wish for more detailed information are referred to the comprehensive studies of Robinson[32], Loomes[26] and Dawson, Drover & Parkes[9].

The transformation of clockmaking from that of a craft into one of a science was effectively triggered by the invention in Holland in the late 1650's of the pendulum and the Fromanteel family, expatriate Dutchmen working in London during the 17th century, were the first to apply this principle to clocks in England. This invention, coupled with the intense interest being shown in Horology by members of the newly formed Royal Society, resulted in rapid advances in clockmaking.

The restoration of the monarchy had given new impetus to an England recovering from Puritan rule and had infused the country with an increasingly relaxed attitude towards luxury and decoration. Owners sought to refurbish their homes, often ravaged by the effects of the Civil War and this stimulated the expansion and proliferation of workshops. From 1658 Ahasuerus Fromanteel advertised clocks for sale, fitted with the new invention and whilst the more traditional clockmakers of the day like Hilderson and East were slower to follow suit, by 1665, most had succumbed to the new methods and style. Other great names came to the fore in the latter part of the 17th century, not least that of Thomas Tompion who benefitted greatly from close collaboration with the scientist Robert Hooke. In his diaries, Hooke makes it clear that Tompion received much guidance and instruction. The relationship floundered on occasion when Tompion was unable to meet the impatient theorist's deadlines and the diaries include such comments as 'Tompion a slug' and 'Tompion a clownish, churlish dog'! Tompion's pre-eminent reputation has overshadowed, somewhat unjustifiably, those of his deservedly famous contemporaries and other clockmakers were taking great strides in the quest for accuracy. The development of the anchor escapement for example, previously thought to have been by William Clement but now attributed to Joseph Knibb, was a further aid to increased accuracy in timekeeping.

There was a prodigious output of clocks during the period 1670-1725 and eminent makers like Daniel Quare and Christopher Gould were also matching Tompion, the Knibbs and East in quantity and sometimes in quality.

Pupils of these great early craftsmen were also making their own contributions to the improvement of clockmaking and two of Tompion's more famous assistants, Edward Banger and George Graham, together with Edward East's best pupil, Henry Jones, have their work represented in the collection.

The bracket clock fashioned by both Tompion and Banger (p.22) during the early years of the 18th century, had formerly been in the collection of Princess Louise, 4th daughter of Queen Victoria, whilst the quality of the clocks by Graham (p.23) and Jones (p.17) confirm the importance of these craftsmen within the context of horology.

The influence of the capital spread afield and many craftsmen, trained in London, moved out into the provinces to establish their own businesses, quickly developing regional styles and traditions. The timepiece by Robert Anderson of Liverpool (p.24) displays most of the features associated with what is popularly known as a 'Lancashire clock' and this longcase clock is an outstanding example of its kind.

# Edward East

**14. Bracket clock,** circa 1665
Edward East, London (1610-1693)
Case: Ebonised Pearwood. Movement: Brass, 8-day
H.17½ (45), W.16 (40), D.8½ (22)

The case has a pedimented top which is supported by Doric columns whilst within, a square matted dial has a narrow silvered chapter-ring pierced between the hours I and II to accommodate a winding arbor for the alarm. This arbor and the two provided for power and strike are shielded from view by shutters linked to a mechanism that is activated when the shutters are pulled aside and which maintains power during the winding operation. The movement has seven baluster-shaped pillars pinned through the back plate and brazed into the front plate framing the wheel trains with massive barrels and a pivoted verge escapement. East's signature in Latin is engraved on the backplate which is mounted with a countwheel that has been engraved with a rosette.

The development of wooden architectural clock cases in England seems to coincide with the return of Charles II. East, along with other clockmakers such as Knibb and the Fromanteels, made many examples of this type.

PROV: George F. H. Hutchinson, Leeds, 1952.

**15. Longcase clock,** circa 1670
Edward East, London (1602-1698)
Case: Walnut; Oak. Movement: Brass, 8-day
H.80 (203), W.15½ (39), D.8 (21)

The 10 inch rectangular face of this piece has a calendar aperture within the matted centre and a narrow chapter-ring made of solid silver mounted onto a brass plate, surrounded by winged cherubs which relate to design no. 4 in Cescinsky and Webster's, *English Domestic Clocks,* 1914, p.91, ff. The movement has an anchor escapement, countwheel strike and bolt-and-shutter maintaining power.

Spirally turned columns support a pedimented top, whilst the door in the trunk is fitted with a lenticle, so that the pendulum bob may be viewed. Patches on the side of the trunk suggest that pouches had been fitted at some stage, to accommodate an increased swing of the pendulum. In 1983 repairs were carried out on the strike work and the hood was restored to rising access.

The longevity of East was quite exceptional. He was official clockmaker to King Charles I at one time and the King sometimes gave one of East's watches as a prize in games of Real Tennis.

PROV: Mallett, 1947.
EXHIB: Temple Newsam, Leeds, *English Clocks,* 1949, no.18.
Science Museum, London, *British Clockmakers,* 1955, no.88.

# Joseph Knibb

**16.  Bracket clock,** circa 1680
Joseph Knibb (active in London 1670-97)
Case: Ebony; oak. Movement: Brass, 8-day
H.11½ (29), W.9 (23), D.6 (15)

The 6¼inch square dial is signed at the base, matted in the centre and has a silvered chapter-ring surrounded by winged cherub spandrels (C&W., no. 2) with engraved acanthus leaf decoration in between. The timepiece movement has a verge escapement, pull repeat that strikes the last previous hour and quarters and a profusely engraved backplate signed, *Joseph Knibb, Londini fecit,* in a slight curve.

The veneered case with its caddy top has re-aligned gilt mounts, four plumed finials and a carrying handle, whilst delicate sound-frets have been incorporated in the side panels and at the top of the door.

PROV: Hansard Watt Collection, Sotheby's, May 26, 1967, lot 3.
ILL: F. J. Britten, *Old Clocks and Watches,* 5th Edition, fig. 476.

**17.  Longcase clock,** circa 1685
Henry Jones, London (active 1663-1695)
Case: Walnut; oak. Movement: Brass, month going
H.74 (188), W.16 (41), D.9 (23)

A 10 inch square dial signed *Henry Jones in the Temple* at the base, with a skeletonised chapter-ring set against a matted background and showing a calendar aperture placed between low set winding holes. The hands and winged cherub spandrels (c&w., no. 4) are consistent with the work of Jones and, within, the movement is pinned throughout, having an anchor escapement, with maintaining power and an externally mounted countwheel strike.

The rising hood, secured by a spoon lock which only releases when the trunk door is opened, is decorated with spiral columns that support a flat cornice, and delicately carved sound-frets in the frieze.

Jones had been an apprentice to Edward East at one time and was one of the leading clockmakers of his age.

PROV: Charles Thornton of York, 1964.
NOTE: R. W. Symonds, *Masterpieces of English Furniture and Clocks,* 1940, p.144, quotes 'Mr. Henry Jones Clockmaker acquainted this court (Clockmakers Company, Jan, 1673) that he having heretofore made for the King (Charles II) a Clock of the value of One Hundred and ffifty Pounds.'

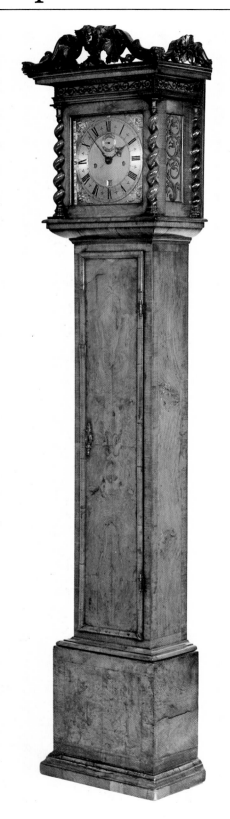

## 18.   Longcase clock, circa 1685-90
Thomas Tompion (active in London 1671-1713)
Case: Walnut; oak. Movement: Brass, Month going
H.82 (209), W.18 (46), D.11 (28)

The 10 inch square dial has an engraved border of double wheatears and a silvered chapter-ring that surrounds a matted centre.

The six pillar movement is fully latched with the trains reversed and having an anchor escapement and an outside countwheel. Whilst the shutter mechanism shielding the winding arbors still operates, the maintaining power bolt is missing.

The veneered case has a forward sliding hood formerly rising, with spiral turned columns supporting a cornice. Above this, a decorated cresting carved with a winged cherub, gargoyles and swagged rosettes is mounted on a broken swan-necked pediment.

PROV: Sir James Lowther, Bt., Flatt, Lancs. By descent through the Earls of Lonsdale. Lowther Castle Sale, April 15, 1947, lot 1226. Charles Thornton of York, 1947.

LIT: Dawson, Drover & Parkes, *Early English Clocks,* 1982, p.269, f.367.

EXHIB: Temple Newsam, Leeds, *English Clocks,* 1949, no. 20.

NOTE: Recorded in 'An Inventory of Household goods belonging to James Lowther Esq at Flatt, taken the 1st June 1724'. 'In the Drawing room, a clock by Tompion.' 'In the gallery and Staircase before the Great Dineing Room'. '1 short Pend$^{\underline{m}}$ Clock by Tompion'.

# Daniel Quare

**19.  Longcase clock,** circa 1690-1700
Daniel Quare, London (1648-1724)
Case: Walnut, oak. Movement: Brass, 8-day
H.94 (239), W.18½ (47), D.10 (26)

This example has an 11 inch square dial, with a matted
centre and an engraved aperture for the date. The rings
around the winding holes were a popular application by
makers such as Quare and the silvered wide chapter-
ring shows half quartermarks engraved in the minute
numeral ring. The plumed mask spandrels (C&W.,
no. 19) were extensively used from about 1700
onwards and whilst the hands are of excellent quality,
they, like the engraving on the chapter-ring, seem
more typical of the work of Christopher Gould.

The veneered case had been lacquered at one time and
the forward sliding hood, formerly rising, with its
hinged door and caddy top, has been considerably
altered at some stage, mostly in the application of a
dummy sounding fret and the re-aligned finials.

Convex mouldings are applied to the throat and
edges and there is a replacement bottle glass in the
lenticle, whilst the skirting substitutes for bun feet.

PROV: Mallett, 1935.
NOTE: Said to have been found in South London, the property of theatrical
people to whom it had been bequeathed by will.

# Daniel Quare

**20.   Bracket clock,** circa 1700, in a later case
Daniel Quare, London (1648-1724)
Case: Boxwood and Rosewood marquetry; oak.
Movement: Brass, 8-day.
H.11 (28), W.11½ (29), D.6 (15)

The 6½ inch square dial is matted in the centre and the two apertures, one for the date and one for the false pendulum, are decorated with scrolled engraving.

Surrounding the silvered chapter-ring are four secondary rings with exposed arbors and they, together with the foliate castings are used instead of the conventional spandrel mounts. The upper set of arbors are intended for regulation and for silent/strike, whilst the bottom set operate an ingenious forked pendulum-locking device that facilitates safe carriage of the clock.

The movement has a verge escapement and a quarter hour repeat pull, operated from one side.

PROV: Mallett, 1937

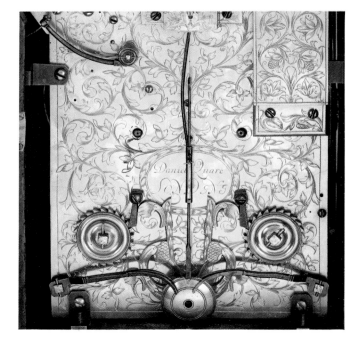

**21. Longcase clock,** circa 1705-10
Joseph Windmills, London (active 1671-1710)
Case: Seaweed marquetry; oak
Movement: Brass, month going
H.91 (232), W.19½ (50), D.10(26)

The 12 inch square dial has a matted centre with a circular calendar aperture, ringed to match the two winding holes, and the silvered chapter-ring is surrounded by cherub and crown spandrels (c&w., no. 8). The wheatear engraved border and elegant pierced hands are consistent with other examples of Windmills' work. The movement has an anchor escapement of 19th century design and has shallow action, together with an outside countwheel strike.

The case front is completely marquetried in arabesque designs with an oval lenticle in the door whilst the caddy top hood, converted from rising to forward sliding access, has pierced sounding frets at the sides and in the frieze.

PROV: D. A. Wetherfield, Esq., Hurcomb's Sale, May 1, 1928, lot 9.
    Percival Griffiths Collection.
    Mallett, 1949.
LIT: F. J. Britten, *The Wetherfield Collection,* 1907, f.74.
W. E. Hurcomb, *The Wetherfield Collection,* 1928, p.23.
R. W. Symonds, *English Furniture from Charles I to George II,* 1929, p.74,
E. Bruton, *The Wetherfield Collection of Clocks,* 1981, p.165, no. 124.
NOTE: The same marquetry design appears on a longcase clock by John Andrews in the collection of Sir John Ramsden, sold Christie's, May 23, 1932, lot 80.

# Tompion & Banger

**22.  Bracket clock,** No. 475, circa 1708
Thomas Tompion & Edward Banger (partnership 1701-08)
Case: Ebony; oak. Movement: Brass, 8-day
H.14½ (37), W.10 (25), D.6½ (17)

The rectangular dial has a false-pendulum aperture within the matted centre and the wide silvered chapter-ring is surrounded by a pair of gilt female mask and scroll spandrels at the base and by subsidiary rings above intended for regulation and strike/silent.

The seven pillar movement is fully latched and has its original crown wheel escapement, plus a partly restored strike and repeat. The elaborately engraved backplate is decorated with interlacing scrolls and foliage and carries the serial No. 475 at its base. The veneered case is also numbered 475 on the front sill.

PROV:  Princess Louise, 1923. 4th dau. of Queen Victoria. Married the 9th Duke of Argyll, sometime Governor General of Canada.
G. F. H. Hutchinson, paid £50.
J. Mason, paid £100. Frodshams, £275. Mallett, £800 in 1946.
EXHIB: Temple Newsam, Leeds, *English Clocks,* 1949, no. 44.
Wembley, London, *British Empire Exhibition,* May, 1923.
NOTE: The dissolution of this partnership was presumably acrimonious as Tompion in his will specifically excluded Banger from his wife's portion, she being Tompion's niece. Banger's career thereafter is obscure. He took on at least one clockmaking apprentice, however, an E. Banger indentured an apprentice in 1715 to train as a leather-worker.

**23. Bracket clock,** No. 753, circa 1720
George Graham, London (1673-1751)
Case: Ebony; oak. Movement: Brass, silver, 8-day
H.14 (35), W.8½ (21), D.6 (15)

The dial of this piece has apertures for a calendar and a false-pendulum, with a silvered wide chapter-ring and silver spandrels, whilst the two subsidiary dials above are intended for the regulation and silent/strike. The fully latched, seven pillar movement with chain drive, has a verge escapement, inside rack strike and pull quarter repeat, whilst the plain backplate is signed *Geo: Graham, London* and stamped with the No. 753.

The veneered case has an inverted-bell top and carrying handle, with glazed break-arch panels to the sides, a pierced sound-fret to the rear door and a smaller panel in the front.

Graham was firstly assistant to and then partner with Thomas Tompion. On the death of his master, Graham took over the business in his own name and continued Tompion's serial numbers. His fame grew and as a Fellow of the Royal Society, he contributed numerous papers published in the *Philosophical Transactions*.

PROV: Asprey, 1973.
ILL: *Antiquarian Horology,* June, 1972, p.581.

# Anderson

**24. Longcase clock,** circa 1775
Robert Anderson, Liverpool
Case: Mahogany; oak. Movement: Brass, 8-day
H.102 (259), W.24 (61), D.10 (26)

The 12 inch arched dial with its date and second hands, has an engraved trelliswork centre with silvered wide chapter-ring surrounded by brass spandrels decorated in the rococo taste. The movement strikes on the quarter hour and, within the arch, illustrated phases of the moon are shown in relation to the 29½ day lunar cycle.

The elaborate case has a forward sliding hood with a scrolled broken pediment and gilt eagle finials supported by pierced Corinthian pilasters, whilst the trunk is decorated with hollow fretted Ionic columns. On the base are representations of rusticated quoins and the whole stands on bracket feet.

PROV: Henry Hirsch Collection, Christie's, June 10-12, 1931, lot 80.
Mallett, 1932.
EXHIB: Science Museum, London, *British Clockmakers,* 1952, no. 170.
LIT: P. Macquoid and R. Edwards, *The Dictionary of English Furniture,* 1st.
edn., 1924, vol. II, p.121, f.57.

**25.  Longcase regulator,** circa 1789
James Boynton of Howden, Yorks. (active 1770-90)
Case: Mahogany. Movement: Brass; silvered dial, 8-day

The circular silvered dial shows the hour, minute and second hands on separate shafts, thus achieving greater accuracy, and the movement has a high count train, dead beat escapement and an iron rod pendulum with micrometer adjustment.

PROV: G. Mawman, Patrington, near Hull, 1839-1881.
      J. S. C., 1881 to 1940, (identity unknown).
      Charles Thornton of York, 1941.

# Watches

**W1.** A silver-cased verge watch, signed Rich Street, London, with large-eared balance-cock, worm-and-rack regulation and signed silver champlevé dial. The single case with its square hinge has the reverse engraved with an equation table and there is a polished steel chain and hinged crank key, circa 1700. 63mm diameter. *page 25 above.*

**W2.** A Swiss silver oignon watch, with bridge-cock movement signed Marchand, à Genève and wound through the enamel dial with central alarm disc, circa 1710. 60mm diameter. *page 25 below.*

**W3.** A French silver pair-cased verge watch with alarm, signed Pierre Durand, has a standing barrel for the alarm and silver champlevé dial with single hand attached to the central alarm disc. The inner case is pierced with an engraved band and split bezel whilst the outer, similarly pierced, has the reverse embossed with a Biblical scene, circa 1720. 56mm diameter.

**W4.** A silver pair-cased rack lever watch, signed Wm. Blanchard, Hull, No. 1212. The balance-cock has a stamped Patent Lever with diamond endstone, plus an enamel dial and plain cases, Birmingham, 1824. 55mm diameter.

**W5.** A Dutch style silver pair-cased verge watch signed Massy, London, No. 2210, pierced balance-cock with the English Royal Achievement, arcaded enamel dial, inner case with split bezel (lacking pendant), outer embossed with scrolls and framing and a badly damaged Huaud School enamel of a woman. 58mm diameter.

**W6.** A Dutch style silver pair-cased verge watch signed J. Britely, London No. 583. It has a silver arcaded champlevé dial, with later alarm disc, inner case plain, outer embossed with a mythological scene, circa 1750. 49mm diameter.

**W7.** A Dutch style silver pair-cased verge watch, signed White, London 1754, with bridge-cock, arcaded enamel dial, inner case plain, outer with classical scene, steel chatelaine suspending two seals and one key. 50mm diameter.

**W8.** A silver repoussé pair-cased verge watch signed Beefield, London No. 5615, Arabic-chaptered enamel dial also signed, inner case plain, outer embossed with a classical scene, circa 1770. 70mm diameter.

**W9.** A silver repoussé pair-cased verge watch signed Peter Smitten, London 212, arcaded enamel dial, inner case plain, outer embossed with a rural figure. 55mm diameter.

**W10.** A giltmetal pair-cased verge watch, signed B. E. May, London, 1782, enamel dial, inner case plain, outer engine-turned. 50mm diameter.

**W11.** A giltmetal pair-cased verge watch, signed Nathl. Sergeant, London No. 51, enamel dial, inner case plain, outer engine-turned.

**W12.** A giltmetal pair-cased verge watch, signed G. W. Wood, May 20th 1759, balance-cock with diamond endstone, enamel dial (damaged) with George W. Wood and Crest for chapters, cases plain, reverse with engraved coat-of-arms. 54mm diameter.

**W13.** A verge watch signed Jas. Wilshire, London 1783, with eared balance-cock, Egyptian pillars, later enamel dial, single tortoiseshell-covered case. 54mm diameter.

**W14.** A giltmetal verge watch signed Le Roy, à Paris, bridge-cock movement, Turkish chaptered enamel dial, case with paste-set bezel, reverse paste-set and partially enamelled. 58mm diameter.

**W15.** A silver verge watch, No. 1758, dust cap, enamel dial, case with engraved cover and reverse (London 1817). 56mm diameter.

**W16.** A silver bridge-cock verge watch with dust cap, signed Philippi Hambourg No. 5601, enamel dial, embossed silver case with steel chain suspending a seal and key (London 1781). 57mm diameter.

**W17.** A giltmetal verge watch by T. Beatson, London, No. 726, diamond endstone, gilt dial with polished chapters, embossed case. 57mm diameter.

**W18.** A further watch, now in the possession of the family was collected by Noel Terry because of its family connections, being a silver pair-cased verge watch, signed *Reuben Terry, York,* with a large-eared balance-cock and silver champlevé dial also signed, *Terry, York.* The cases are plain with a split bezel on the inner and chamfered hinge on the outer, circa 1715. Reuben Terry is recorded working in York from 1713 to 1724.

# Furniture

The alphabetical and chronological sequence of this section has been determined by the dual factors of function and the popularly accepted description of each piece. Where there are multi-purpose items, then either the primary function, or the term used in the *Dictionary of English Furniture*[10] has governed its classification.

In viewing the collection, it would be misleading to think that it represents a cross-section of all English furniture fashioned during the last 350 years. The conservative taste of this Yorkshire gentleman was bound to influence the selection, to the extent that early oak, gilded or painted furniture had no appeal to him, whereas carved mahogany undoubtedly did. It was this single-minded concentration, however, which gives the collection its great strength and allowed him to build it up over a remarkably long period of time. Noel Terry had much in common with other true collectors of his day, like Percival Griffiths, who also found it difficult to resist the acquisition of a rare or unusual piece. Whether a place could be found for it at home was, to both, a minor consideration and in later years, as furniture vans continued to turn up at 'Goddards' laden with another large piece of furniture, it was Mrs. Terry's practice to remind her husband about the lack of space left in the body of the house and that it would have to go into the attic.

His serious collecting started in 1926 with the acquisition of an armchair (no. 58) and he was still collecting in 1978 when he acquired the pair of torchères (no. 123), both very much in the Chippendale tradition. He left a carefully worked out code that gave the year of purchase and supplier, plus a record of the cost based on a numerical code that used the word 'Prudential' as the key. Thus F18M35TAL translates to: Bought from Mallet in 1935 for £790.

What this code does, in fact, is to offer a fascinating glimpse of Noel Terry's developing taste and connoisseurship, whilst at the same time providing an extremely valuable basis for future research into the provenance of the collection.

Glancing through the lists, it can be seen that Noel Terry flirted with some early walnut and the occasional piece of oak, but developed his taste for good mahogany furniture very early on. Neither was he distracted by gilt, painted or lacquered furniture, despite a very early purchase of a lacquered chest of drawers (no. 87).

As an extremely busy executive director of the family firm, it was difficult for him to create time to attend the great country house sales of the 1930's and 40's and he much preferred to place his trust in a few reputable dealers who were able to keep him in touch with current developments. During the late 1940's and 50's however, his business activities took him down to London regularly and he was able to view many of the important sales being held in the auction rooms of Christie's and Sotheby's. Mallett's were used on these occasions, but this time as agents, bidding for Noel Terry on the day of the sale. Gradually, over the years, he began creating his own personal sample collection and in it he brought together individual masterpieces, both major and minor, rather than attempting to assemble the balanced furnishings of a period house. Many of the pieces of case furniture are elaborately fitted out with drawers for writing and dressing and the eye of the discerning collector is apparent, choosing something just a little different.

Some of the exceptional pieces that he acquired, in addition to the splendid anthology of clocks and barometers, include the Dressing Commode (no. 81) attributed to Chippendale, that came from Kimbolton Castle in Huntingdonshire. This piece, like several others in the collection, had crossed the Atlantic and formed part of the Walter J. Chrysler Collection before 1976.

One of the better known pieces in the collection, illustrated in many of the standard text books, is the kneehole writing desk (no. 105) fashioned in the gothic taste. This example was shown, with a number of Noel Terry's pieces in the 1951 exhibition of Chippendale furniture at Temple Newsam.

Chairs are well represented and the highlight must be the pair of armchairs (no. 59) attributed to the workshops of John Gordon, which were probably commissioned by the 4th Earl of Cardigan and his wife, Lady Mary Montagu, for Ditton Park, a 17th century house in Buckinghamshire.

Tables are another popular feature and range from the extravagantly carved card table (no.113) possibly supplied by Joseph Ward to the Dukes of Northumberland, through to the extraordinary pair of tables (no. 121) that came from Hartwell House in Buckinghamshire.

It was, however, the finely carved secretaire-cabinet (no. 97) with its elaborate fretwork and semi-secret drawers hidden in the frieze, that was considered by Noel Terry to be the prize of his collection. It was previously owned by Lady Dudley Ward and is attributed to the workshops of the celebrated William Vile.

# Bellows

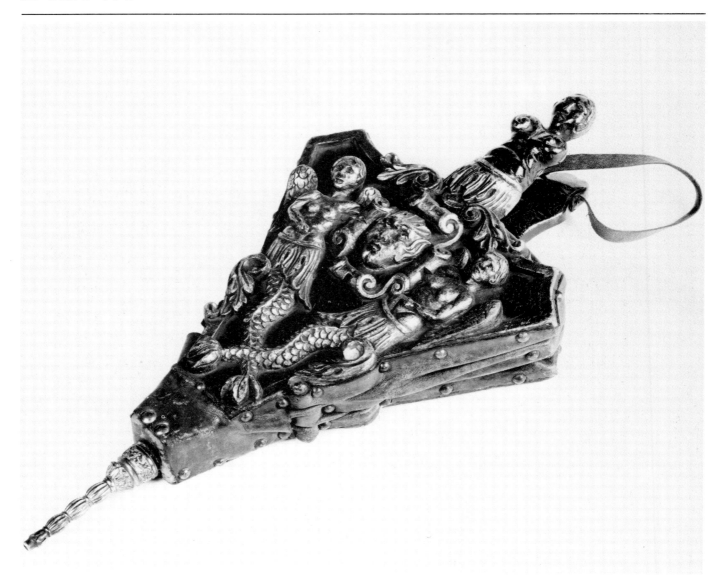

**28.  Bellows,** Continental, circa 1580
Walnut; leather. L.19(48), W.10 (25)

A pair of walnut and parcel-gilt bellows fashioned in
the style of 16th and 17th century examples seen in
Italy and France. The two boards are richly embossed
with 'Mannerist' faces and figures and the reverse has
a horned mask surrounded by leaf scrolls whilst the eyes
have been cleverly pierced to function as the vent holes.

On the front there is an intricate arrangement of
winged mermaids supporting a cartouche, and at the
centre, a long-eared face presumably personifying one
of the four great winds.

PROV: Charles Thornton of York, 1948.

**29.  Box,** Polish, circa 1735-40
Walnut. H.6 (15), W.12 (30), D.7½ (19)

An 18th century box carved with effigies of Polish
Kings and Queens. The carved figures are arranged in
panels on all sides, starting at 550 AD with King
Lechus I and culminating on the top of the lid with the
two Kings, Augustus II 1697 and Augustus III 1733.
They are shown dressed in full armour, and standing
within a balustraded colonnade which has been hung
with tassels. Borders of acanthus leaf and imperial
cartouches filled with messages or medallions complete
the carved detail.

PROV: Charles Thornton of York, 1940.

# Buffet

**30. Buffet,** English, circa 1610
Oak; various fruitwoods
H.48½ (123), W.51 (130), D.17½ (45)

A splay-fronted top section is decorated with inlaid floral designs on panels which have been deeply recessed and set in wide carved mouldings. There are massive bulbous supports with Ionic capitals on both top and bottom sections and the top pair, carved with inter-lacing foliate designs, support an inlaid frieze with faces on the corbels. The lower frieze is formed into a drawer and carved with lions' masks.

PROV: William Randolph Hearst, Christie's, May 18, 1939, lot 107. Mallett, 1939.
EXHIB: Victoria and Albert Museum, London, *B.A.D.A. Art Treasures Exhibition,* 1932, no. 14.
CF.: A strikingly similar example belonging to Sir Charles Lawes-Wittewronge, Bt., was sold at Christie's on May 14, 1936, lot 116.

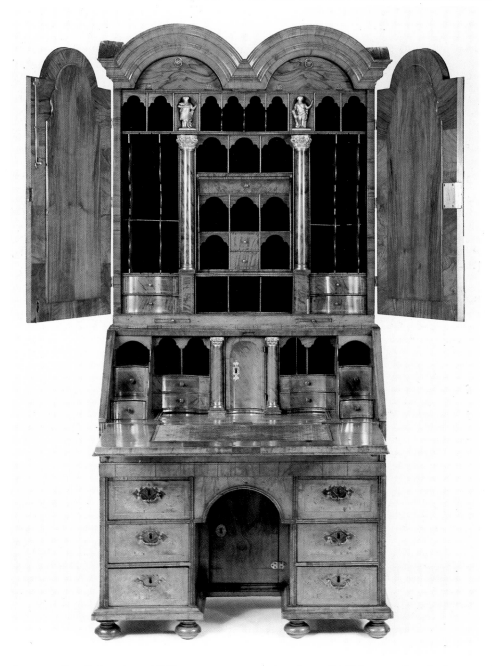

**31. Bureau bookcase,** English, circa 1700
Walnut; oak; pine
H.84½ (215), W.41 (104), D.24½ (62)

The upper bookcase has moulded panels in the doors
and they enclose an interior fitted out with curved
drawers, vertical compartments and Corinthian
columns which are embellished with parcel-gilt brass
mounts supporting a pair of gilded Roman figures. A

pair of candleslides are fitted above a fall front which
opens to reveal a similar arrangement to that above.
Behind the columns and false structures are eleven
secret drawers.

PROV: R. A. Lee, 1934.
      Mallett, 1935.
LIT: *Apollo*, June, 1935.
NOTE: A £1 banknote drawn on the Cheltenham and Gloucestershire bank
in 1820, was discovered behind one of the secret drawers.

# Bureau

**32. Bureau,** English, circa 1705-10
Walnut; oak; pine
H.39 (89), W.34½ (88), D.21 (54)

The writing compartment is fitted with pigeon holes, drawers and secret compartments in the well and has convex mouldings applied to the edges which are repeated on the drawer surrounds below.

Two long and two short drawers have herringbone inlay at their edges and are fitted with plain brass ring handles and escutcheon plates. The term bureau as distinguished from that of desk and cabinet, was not used in England before the end of the 17th century and the description presumably gained credibility during the reign of William and Mary. It was known and described as a 'chest of drawers with a writing board' and very much in evidence on the Continent, well before the return of Charles II to the English throne.

PROV: Mallett, 1934.

# Dressing Bureau

**33.  Dressing bureau,** English, circa 1715
Walnut; pine
H.68½ (174), W.26 (66), D.17 (43)

The beginning of the 18th century saw an amalgamation of the more traditional English escritoire or desk on stand with that of the bureau and resulted in the development of pieces such as these, often with their own stands and sometimes fitted with a dressing glass on top. The multi-purpose nature of such pieces, with the writing bureau below and dressing glass above, made them suitable contenders for the Dressing room.

The gentleman of the house would greet visitors in a Dressing room, whilst leisurely preparing himself for the day ahead and if interrupted by a tradesman during his toilet, could write a note or letter without unduly disturbing himself.

A gentleman's Dressing room was usually situated on the ground floor, to prevent 'people of that kind' from coming upstairs, whereas the lady's Dressing room was normally found on the first floor, close to the bedroom and intended for entertaining during the long, arduous hours of their toilet preparation.

The interior of the bureau is fitted with pigeon holes and has a centre compartment flanked by fluted pilasters that conceal a pair of secret drawers.

Below the writing top are two drawers, both veneered in burr-walnut and one has a shaped concave front. An interesting feature of these drawers is the way walnut is used instead of the more normal oak or pine to fashion the linings.

The plain stand has simple but elegant cabriole legs and the pad feet have been recessed underneath to house castors. A bevelled glass is fitted on top and is housed in a walnut frame with gilt-gesso surrounds. The width of this example is only 26ins, and suggests that it was intended to stand in a pier, between windows.

PROV: The Tremayne family, Heligan, St. Austell, Cornwall.
    Charles Thornton of York, 1947.
LIT: R. W. Symonds, *Antique Collector,* May/June, 1950, p.107, f.3.
P. Macquoid and R. Edwards, *The Dictionary of English Furniture,* rev.edn., 1954, vol.I, p.132, f.20.

# Dressing Bureau

**34.   Dressing bureau,** English, circa 1735
Mahogany; pine; oak
H.76 (193), W.32 (81), D.20 (56)

The fall front drops to reveal a traditional bureau arrangement and the stand is embellished with egg and dart moulding to the top, shell and leaf decoration to the underframe and ringed lions' masks at the knees of the cabriole legs. At the back of the knee the leg is cleverly undercut to accentuate the form, and hanging from the lions' mouth are flowering pendants which trail down the leg towards the hairy paw feet.

The dressing glass is unbevelled and the frame, with its architectural broken pediment, is enriched with egg and dart mouldings.

PROV: Glover of Haslemere, 1949.
          Mallett, 1950.
LIT: R. W. Symonds, *Antique Collector,* May/June, 1950, p.109, f.5.
*Country Life,* 1950, vol.107, p.1719, f.7.
EXHIB: Grosvenor House, Antique Dealers Fair, 1950, p.67.

**35. Bureau bookcase,** English, circa 1775
attributed to the workshop of Thomas Chippendale
Mahogany; pine
H.96 (244), W.80 (203), D.23 (58)

The four panel doors are glazed in a geometric pattern
and surmounted by a concave cornice, fringed with
delicate fretwork.

The base has a central cupboard enclosing further
drawers and above there is a secretaire section with a
fall front supported on quadrant brackets. Flanking this
is a set of ten drawers, inlaid with ivory, showing the
letters A to K and each drawer is mounted with an
intricate lion's mask and drop-ring handle. The arrangement of the drawers would suggest that the bookcase
was intended as one of a pair.

PROV: Charles Thornton of York, 1947.
CF.: A pair of bookcases inlaid with the same compass medallions were
supplied by Chippendale for Pembroke House, circa 1760-62. (C. Gilbert,
*The Life and Work of Thomas Chippendale*, 1978, vol.2, f.68-9).

# Bureau Bookcase

**36. Bureau bookcase,** English, circa 1790
Mahogany; pine; oak
H.96½ (245), W.85½ (217), D.25 (64)

The cabinet is glazed in the gothic taste but with an unusual swagged treatment of the central glazing bars. The inside of each door had been hung with silk at one time and the cornice above has been arcaded.

In the base, a series of drawers and sliding trays surround a plain secretaire section.

PROV: Mallett of Bath, 1931.
CF.: A bookcase with similar decorative features was sold at Sotheby's, Nov. 18-19, 1937, lot 275.

**37.  Bureau bookcase,** English, circa 1790
Mahogany; pine; oak
H.86 (218), W.38 (97), D.20 (51)

The two panelled doors are glazed in a geometric pattern and were hung at some time with silk on the inside. Above, a fluted frieze supports a delicate dentil cornice and below the piece is fitted with a traditional bureau arrangement of small drawers, pigeon-holes and fluted pilasters.

Replacement handles and escutcheons in the rococo style are fitted to the drawers and fall front.

PROV: Charles Thornton of York, 1946.

# Bureau Bookcase

**38.  Bureau bookcase,** English, circa 1795
Mahogany; pine; oak
H.86 (218), W.43 (100), D.22½ (57)

The two panelled doors are glazed in geometric patterns reminiscent of Chippendale's designs and the cornice is veneered to imitate a dentil moulding with a frieze banded by herringbone inlay. The fall front opens to reveal small drawers, pigeon-holes and secret compartments concealed by fluted columns. Below are four drawers fitted with their original drop-ring handles and the whole piece stands on simple bracket feet.

PROV: V, 1918 (identity unknown).

**39. Cabinet,** English, circa 1690-95
Kingwood; pine; oak
H.65 (166), W.47 (120), D.21 (54)

Construction is in two parts with the top section having a pair of doors enclosing a series of small drawers and a central cupboard. The pulvinated frieze above is fashioned as a drawer and the double doors in the bottom section open to reveal shelves.

The cabinet retains its original brass fitments and the hinges on the doors are strengthened by the use of cross lateral fixings.

This type of decoration, known as oyster-cut veneering, is created by the juxtaposition of slices of timber which have been cut at an angle, across the bough of a tree. It was a very effective and altogether cheaper alternative to the intricate floral marquetry decoration being employed at that time.

These cabinets and chests must have had a remarkable appearance when new, as evidenced by the interior of the top section which has not been exposed to the effects of light.

PROV: Mallett, 1935.

# Cabinet on Stand

**40. Cabinet on stand,** English, circa 1695
Seaweed marquetry; pine; oak
H.64 (163), W.44½ (113), D.20½ (52)

Veneered with panels of seaweed marquetry, set within
a field of oyster-cut laburnum and bordered by an
interlinking boxwood inlay. The doors enclose a series
of small drawers below a pulvinated frieze.

PROV: Cora, Countess of Strafford and on loan to the Victoria and Albert
Museum for some time.
LIT: P. Macquoid, *The Age of Walnut,* 1923, p.129, f.120.
EXHIB: Landsdowne House, London, *English Decorative Art,* February,
1929, no.259.
CF.: A similar example, with only minor variations, on display at
Chatsworth House, Derbyshire. Also a pair of side tables, the property
of the Earls of Chesterfield, Holme Lacy, Hertfordshire, which match the
base section in construction and decorative detail, were sold by Knight,
Frank and Rutley on Jan. 31, 1910, lot 583.

**41. Cabinet on stand,** English, circa 1700-05
Carcass: Oak; walnut
Veneer: Walnut; fruitwoods; ivory
H.65½ (166), W.49½ (126), D.82 (51)

The fall front of this escritoire is veneered with medallions of floral marquetry set within scrolled leaf cartouches and further bouquets of flowers are inlaid into the spandrels. Above, the frieze contains the usual drawer, but has a concave shape in contrast to the previous example on page 40 and highlights a stylistic change that took place at the beginning of the 18th century. The interior of the cabinet with its many secret drawers is illustrated on page 42.

PROV: Mallett, 1947.

# Cabinet on Stand

The fall front, supported by iron elbow hinges, drops to reveal an intricate arrangement of pigeon-holes, drawers and cupboards decorated with the same floral marquetry, plus an astonishing number of secret compartments. Banks, as such, did not exist as we know them today and it must have been very necessary to secrete one's valuables and documents at home, away from the 'thieving hands of the servants'.

The ingenious arrangements employed by craftsmen to create such masterpieces, must have also helped them in the selling of their wares with the only hope being, that having revealed the wealth of secrets to a prospective buyer, the cabinet-maker did not suffer the same fate as befell the tomb builders of ancient Egypt.

Of the 48 drawers and pigeon-holes in this cabinet, 21 are intended to be secret and are shown in total on the writing board. Some elaborate tricks have been employed to disguise their presence and the only danger was that precious items could be 'lost' or forgotten by the family if the owner died unexpectedly.

Double drawers at the side pull out to reveal containers for ink-pots and quills, whilst the whole of the lower section draws out in order to gain access to a series of secret slides behind. In addition, a small cupboard in the centre cleverly conceals another series of compartments by making the locking pegs that hold the false panel in place part of the construction.

Set within the fall front a hinged platform can be raised for reading and used whilst standing.

J. T. Smith in *Nollekens and his Times* records that John Cobb, partner to the royal cabinet-maker William Vile, was the first to introduce a 'convenient' table which was 'so healthy for those who stand to write, read or draw'. A very rich diet and copious quantities of drink must have wreaked havoc on the digestion and perhaps made it more comfortable to stand.

NOTE: Items discovered in this cabinet to date: a pair of Chinese silver sanding pots, an early bronze figure of a satyr, a bronze figure of Pan and a Milner's safe key!

**43. Dressing cabinet,** English, circa 1760-65
Mahogany. H.82 (208), W.41 (105), D.24 (61)

A serpentine-fronted base standing on shaped bracket feet. The top drawer converts to a writing slide which, when pushed back, reveals an elaborately fitted dressing compartment with an adjustable mirror and containers for boxes, etc;

The upper section has a central glazed compartment with rebates for shelves and is flanked by two other cupboards, whilst above, there is a delicate arrangement of fretted galleries and finials.

PROV: R. M. Broadhead, Esq., Ockwells Manor, Berks.
    Hotspur of London, 1977.
ILL: *Connoisseur,* June, 1966, p.LI.

# Bureau Cabinet

**44.   Bureau cabinet,** English, circa 1770
Mahogany; pine
H.87 (221),  W.40 (102),  D.17½ (45)

The writing board is supported on quadrant brackets and the interior is fitted with pigeon-holes and drawers lined with mahogany.

The Chinese influence can be seen in the fluted edge, carved to represent a pagoda roof and the glazed cabinet is fitted out for shelves whilst nail holes on the inside of the doors suggest that they were hung with silk at some time. A broken arched pediment, formed by linking 'C' scrolls, has a pierced trellis fretwork infill and the central space between may well have been intended for the display of an urn or bust.

PROV: Mallett, 1947.
CF.: A similar cabinet from the Capel Cure Collection, (R. Edwards and P. Macquoid, *The Dictionary of English Furniture,* rev.edn., 1954, vol.I, p.151, f.59). Both pieces have a strong affinity with the workshop of William Vile.

**45.   Dwarf cabinet,** English, circa 1800
Mahogany; pine
H.59 (150), W.24 (61), D.16 (41)

The double doors of the cabinet, which had been lined with silk at some time, have beaded brass edging and are glazed in the gothic taste, using a design illustrated in Thomas Shearer's *Designs for Household Furniture* (1788).

Rebates are cut within to support shelves and the cornice is decorated with arcading.

An unusual base has narrow tapered legs, supported by pierced spandrel brackets and the single drawer to the front is fitted with stamped brass handles showing the remains of blue enamel medallions at their centres.

This type of small cabinet was often intended for the Boudoir or the Drawing room and used for the display of china.

PROV: Charles Thornton of York, 1941.

# Chair

**46.  Chair,** one of two, English, circa 1695
Walnut with upholstered seat
H.53½ (136), W.21 (54), D.21 (54)

Their shape and arrangement show an affinity to the designs of Daniel Marot[28] but with a particularly English treatment of the carving seen on the pierced splat and in the arrangement of the plain baluster legs linked by cross-shaped serpentine stretchers.

Huguenot craftsmen, driven out of Europe by religious persecution during the 17th century, flocked to England in search of work and the inevitable cross-fertilization of ideas soon became apparent in the products of the English workshops. These chairs were an early purchase (1934) and ideal for Goddards with its 'old world' country house charm. Noel Terry often enjoyed telling the tale about his great urge to 'clean them up'. Close inspection of the two *in situ* will reveal that he had started doing so on the crest of one and it was only the intervention of Charles Thornton that stayed Noel Terry's hand and prevented him from removing the patination of centuries.

PROV: Sir E. H. Scott, Bt., Westbury Manor, Brackley, Sotheby's, June 12, 1931, lot 18.
Mallett, 1934.

46

**47.  Chair,** possibly English, circa 1705-10
Walnut with upholstered seat
H.47 (120), W.20 (50), D.22 (56)

The waisted splat is curved with the comfort of the sitter in mind and has been elaborately carved with fishscale decoration, trellis hatching and husks, presumably in imitation of Chinese designs.

The front legs are of cabriole form, a term taken from a French dancing word meaning 'to bound or to leap'. They have been embellished at the knee with shell and husk motifs and stand on voluted feet, whilst on the back legs, the severe lines have been softened by use of a gentle scrolled decoration.

In 1717 Thomas Roberts supplied chairs of a similar nature to Hampton Court Palace, describing them as having 'India Backs'. This may well have been a generic term implying a Far Eastern influence, in the same way that suppliers of wallpaper were using the term 'mock India' papers, to describe block printed wallpapers decorated with Far Eastern designs.

PROV: R. A. Lee, 1935.
    Mallett, 1937.
CF.: A similar chair illustrated in the *Catalogue van Meubelen, Rijksmuseum, Amsterdam,* 1952 and listed as coming from the North-Netherlands.

# Stool

**48. Stool,** English, circa 1720
Walnut; parcel-gilt, with needlework seat
H.17 (43), W.28 (71), D.19½ (50)

This example, fashioned in walnut, has elaborate ringed cabriole legs which stand on ball and claw feet. The gilded carving has acanthus leaf decoration at the knee and bowed eagle heads supporting the seat. On the seat, the replacement gros-point needlework illustrates two women picking flowers in a garden, attended by sheep, and although the needlework has been considerably repaired at some stage, it still retains many of its original features. These stools were not normally ordered on their own, but usually formed a part of a large set, intended for use by guests at important state occasions. These large sets would invariably be arranged against the walls of the room and the stools are shown flanking the fireplace or placed in the bay of the window.

PROV: A. C. Hunter, Esq., Bystock, Exmouth.
Charles Thornton of York, 1945.
ILL: F. Lenygon, *Furniture in England 1660-1760,* 1st edn., 1904, f.116, en suite with an upholstered chair f.64. An extraordinary armchair from the same set, now on display in the State Dining Room at Chatsworth House, Derbyshire, is illustrated by the same author in her companion volume, *Decoration in England 1640-1760,* 1922, f.188.

**49.  Chair,** one of four, English, circa 1720
Walnut with needlework seat
H.42 (107), W.22½ (57), D.25 (63)

The wide compass-shaped drop-in seats are upholstered in contemporary needlework, showing scenes which seem to depict four stages of courtship.

Burr-walnut is used on the vase-shaped splat, and the front legs are of cabriole form standing on ball and claw feet. This decorative treatment was introduced from about 1710 onwards and no doubt derives its sources from oriental antiquity.

Each chair has been stamped underneath with the letters R.W. and the inside of the seat rails are marked with Roman numerals.

PROV:  Percival Griffiths, Esq.
        Guy Charrington, Esq., 1941.
        Ginsburg & Levy, New York, 1966.
        Hotspur, 1975.
LIT:  R. W. Symonds, *Masterpieces of English Furniture,* 1940, p.1, f.1.
R. W. Symonds, *Connoisseur,* Sept., 1934, p.169.
CF.:  A double chair back settee from the collection of Sir E. H. Scott, Bt., Westbury Manor, Brackley, sold Sotheby's, June 12, 1931, is probably part of the same set.

# Stool

**50. Stool,** English, circa 1720
Walnut with petit-point needlework
H.16 (40), W.22 (56), D.19½ (50)

The cabriole legs have flower and leaf decoration at the knee and they stand on club feet.

It is interesting to compare the extent of carved ornamentation applied to these domestic pieces made in walnut with that applied to those constructed of mahogany in later years. John Evelyn, the famous 17th century diarist, wrote in his book *Sylva* (1644) that whilst recognising the importance of walnut in furniture making, it should be noted that most English walnut was too open grained for intricate carving.

Only by importing the finest walnut from France, Italy and Spain, could the carver create the elaborate decorative motifs and patterns being introduced as a result of the relaxed mood of the Restoration.

A severe frost in 1704[2] destroyed many of the walnut trees in England and foreign walnut had become scarcer and more expensive, with the result that craftsmen made greater use of veneers in their efforts to economise. By 1720 the supply of Continental walnut had virtually dried up, caused in part by the government imposing a tax of £8 per ton on imported timber and an alternative source of supply was sought.

PROV: Charles Thornton of York, 1931.

**51. Armchair,** English, circa 1725
Walnut with contemporary upholstery
H.35 (89), W.30 (76), D.32 (82)

The splayed cabriole legs are carved with lions' masks at the knee and are representative of a fashionable decorative motif used during the second quarter of the 18th century. The mask is finished off under the seat in wide scrolled brackets and spouting from the lion's mouth are garlands of leaves trailing down the leg towards the club foot.

Comparison with the bureau dressing table No. 34 will reveal a similar motif applied at the knee but executed in a much more sophisticated manner. The material used in that instance is mahogany, a close grained timber which, despite needing much stronger tools to carve it, had many advantages over walnut.

This ability to receive fine carved detail made it an ideal material to cope with the developing styles of the 18th century.

# Armchair

**52. Armchair,** English, circa 1735
Mahogany with velvet upholstery
H.44 (102), W.29½ (75), D.36 (92)

The bold cabriole legs are richly decorated with a flowering rosette contained within a hatched shield at the knee and the hairy paw feet on which they stand had originally been fitted with castors.

Unusual features of this chair are the carved rosettes and trailing garlands decorating the arms.

The use of mahogany, although known in England as early as the 1670's, only became popular from about 1725 onwards when large quantities were being shipped in from San Domingo and Jamaica as an alternative to the more expensive walnuts from France, Italy and Spain. From 1722 to 1743 the government, under Walpole, allowed the import of timber from Jamaica free of all duty[2]. This was intended to apply to indigenous timber felled on the shores of the island. However, traders smuggled mahogany through Jamaica and sold it under the banner of the colony. It had been seen not only as a means of generating trade with the colonies, but perhaps as a foil to the embargo placed on the export of the best walnut from France.

PROV: Mallett, 1945.

**53.  Chair,** one of two, English, circa 1740
Mahogany with petit-point needlework seat
H.39 (99), W.25½ (65), D.23½ (60)

The bold cabriole legs have been richly carved with an open flower and cabochon centre at the knee and have hairy paw feet at the front.

On the back, the stiles are fluted and enclose a pierced, vase-shaped splat which has been richly decorated with interlacing and carved with flowers and foliage, whilst the top rail is embellished on the cresting with a massive scallop-shell and further scrolled decoration.

PROV: Lord Savile, Rufford Abbey, Notts, sold on the premises by Knight, Frank and Rutley, October 11, 1938, Lot 106 (a set of eight).
Mallett, 1952.

ILL: *Country Life,* 1903, vol.14, p.650.

CF.: Strikingly similar to a set of six sold from the Collection of Sir E. J. Dean Paul, Bt., Cambridge House, Twickenham, at Christie's on 10 March, 1896, lot 810.
An armchair of similar form but with minor variations on the interlaced splat was sold at Sotheby's on 19 July, 1974, lot 104.

NOTE: Rufford Abbey, a Cistercian Monastery prior to the dissolution, was converted to a country mansion by the Earl of Shrewsbury, husband of Bess of Hardwick and considerably enlarged and re-built in the 1680's by Sir George Savile, Bt., subsequently created Marquis of Halifax. In 1784 the estates were to pass to the son of the Earl of Scarbrough and his wife Barbara Savile.

# Armchair

**54.  Armchair,** English, circa 1750
Mahogany with contemporary upholstery
H.40 (101), W.26½ (67), D.29 (74)

The short, bold cabriole legs are carved with acanthus
leaf decoration at the knee and the scrolled toes have the
same treatment rising from the pad feet.

   The use of an acanthus leaf motif in architecture and
decoration is a conventional representation of
'Acanthus Spinosus' a native of the Mediterranean
countries and this foliage is seen employed on the
capitals of the Corinthian and Composite orders.

It was first freely used on furniture in England
during the early Renaissance (1420-1500) then widely
exploited as a motif during the late Stuart period
(1660-1700) and again after the introduction of
mahogany in the 1730's.

PROV: Charles Thornton of York, 1938.
CF.: A set of six chairs and a daybed with the same carved detail were sold
at Hoar Cross, Staffs., by H. Spencer and Sons, June 24-28, 1952, lots
30 and 711.
NOTE: The Meynells of Hoar Cross have strong family connections with
the Ingram family, former owners of Temple Newsam, Leeds. The
Yorkshire estates passed by descent through the female line from Charles,
9th Viscount Ingram (d.1778) and it was Elizabeth, 3rd eldest daughter
who married Hugo Meynell.

**55. Armchair,** one of three, English, circa 1750-55
Mahogany; pine with upholstered seat
H.37 (94), W.25 (64), D.26 (66)

These chairs would seem to be of pre-*Director* design, incorporating many of the stylistic treatments of the period which Chippendale was to highlight in *The Gentleman and Cabinet-maker's Director,* 1754.

The quality of the chair illustrated is superior to that of the other two in the set and displays a greater sense of clarity and movement in the carved detail. The bold cabriole legs are carved with leaf and foliage motifs on the knee and stand on dolphins' heads, a popular treatment of the French rococo.

PROV: Sir E. J. Dean Paul, Bt., Christie's, March 10, 1896, lot 811 (2).
Leopold Hirsch, Esq., Christie's, May 7, 1934, lot 37 (2).
Pierpont Morgan, Esq., Christie's, March 22, 1944, lot 99 (2).
Ernest Raphael, Esq., Christie's, Nov. 9, 1945, lot 163.
Mallett, 1945.
The third chair probably came from Mrs. A. Foster, Basset Down, Wilts.
LIT: *Country Life,* 1928, vol.64, p.642.
EXHIB: Burlington Fine Arts Club, 1919.
Temple Newsam, Leeds, *Thomas Chippendale,* 1951, no.109.
Cannon Hall, Barnsley, *Chippendale Furniture,* 1963, no.36.

# Chair

**56.  Chair,** one of four, English, circa 1760
Mahogany; pine; with upholstered seat
H.37 (94), W.22½ (57), D.21½ (55)

This type of chair with its fluted stiles and 'Owl's-eye' splat was popular during the third quarter of the 18th century, although not apparently illustrated in the traditional pattern books of the day.

There is a hint of gothic tracery at the base of the splat with exaggerated gadrooning on the waist, whilst the stiles on the back are fluted and have carved garlands applied at the junction with the top-rail.

PROV: Elson of London, 1934.
        Charles Thornton of York, 1935.
EXHIB: Grosvenor House, Antique Dealers Fair, October, 1934.
LIT: A. Carfax, *Connoisseur*, November, 1934, p.329.
CF.: The set have strong similarities with some chairs formerly at Great Maytham Hall and now in the family pew of the Gybbon-Moneypennys at St. Mary's Church, Rolvenden, Kent.
Other English pieces showing only minor variations to the legs and splat are illustrated in: Morrison Heckscher, *American Furniture at the Metropolitan Museum*, 1984, vol.2, p.74, f.33 and John T. Kirk, *Visual Survey of British and American Furniture*, 1982, p.266, f.932.

**57. Armchair,** English, circa 1760-65
Mahogany; pine; upholstered seat and back
H.41 (104), W.30½ (77), D.25 (63)

Chippendale's design for a 'French chair' in the rococo taste was no doubt the inspiration for this armchair, although the craftsman chose to ignore the advice that 'some (chairs) are intended to be open below the back'.

The 22 inch wide blue damask covering has replaced the original tapestry and repairs to the seat rails and feet were carried out at some time following the International Art Treasures Exhibition of 1962.

PROV: Frederick Howard Reed, Esq., Hay Hill, London W1.
W. Waddingham, 1960.
Hotspur, 1962 and 1975.
EXHIB: Victoria and Albert Museum, *International Art Treasures Exhibition,* 1962, no.109.
CF.: D. Fitz-Gerald, *Georgian Furniture,* 1968, f.59.

# Armchair

**58.  Armchair,** English, circa 1760-65
Mahogany with upholstered seat
H.40 (101), W.25½ (65), D.23½ (60)

The chair closely resembles a design shown in the *Director* (1st edn., 1754, pl.X) and in the supplementary notes, Chippendale counsels 'that the seats look best when stuffed over the rails and that they are commonly finished using one or two rows of brass nails.' In addition he recommends that they are usually covered with the same 'stuff' as the window curtains.

Christopher Gilbert[12] argues that it would be difficult to exaggerate the effect that *The Gentleman and Cabinet-maker's Director,* published by Thomas Chippendale in 1754 had on the style of furniture in the mid-18th century. Over half of the original 308 subscribers were either cabinet-makers or allied tradesmen and they clearly saw the emergence of this catalogue as a very valuable source of ideas.

The Chippendale designs proliferated and other cabinet-makers like Ince and Mayhew, keen to establish their own reputation followed suit with their own publications[18]. Some of their designs seem to be blatant copies taken from the *Director* but others show a distinct, individual flair.

PROV: Albert Amor, 1926.
EXHIB: Temple Newsam, Leeds, *Thomas Chippendale,* 1951, no.110.

**59. Armchair,** one of two, English, circa 1760
Attributed to the workshop of John Gordon
Mahogany; beech; with upholstered back and seat
H.38½ (98), W.28½ (72), D.31½ (80)

The stuffed arched backs and upholstered seats are
linked by curved arms and inswept supports, carved
with a double band of fishscaling and this imbrication
is repeated on the shaped seat rails and cabriole legs.

At the front, tapering panels of husks and foliage
trail down from the knee, whilst each foot has a shaped
'French' toe, carved with a rising leaf and they stand on
deep, inset castors.

PROV: Ditton Park, Buckinghamshire. Probably ordered by George
Brudenell, 4th Earl of Cardigan (1712-90) and his wife Lady Mary
Montagu, heiress to Ditton Park, a 17th century country house,
from John, 2nd Duke of Montagu.
By descent through The Dukes of Buccleuch to The Lords
Montagu of Beaulieu.
Mallett, 1949.

LIT: H. Cescinsky, *English Furniture of the 18th Century,* 1910, vol.2, f.392,
records a set of twenty four armchairs and a settee *(sic)* arranged in the
long corridors of Ditton Park. Eight armchairs and two settees from this
set were part of the Walter P. Chrysler, Jn. Collection and sold by Parke-
Bernet Galleries, New York on May 6-7, 1960, lots 520-525.

CF.: A. Coleridge, *Chippendale Furniture,* 1968, p.182, f.87, illustrates one
from a set of eight sidechairs with the same imbricated decoration supplied
by John Gordon to the 2nd Duke of Atholl in 1756.
A similar set were also supplied by Gordon and Taitt for Spencer House
and they are now on display at Althorp.

# Armchair

**60. Armchair,** English, circa 1760-65
Mahogany with upholstered seat and back
H.36 (92), W.29 (74), D.33 (84)

The splayed arms are decorated with an unusual
cabochon motif, whilst the sides of the seat rail are
carved with leaf, shell and wave designs. Short cabriole
legs have combined leaf and scroll toes and are fitted
with replacement brass castors.

PROV: Charles Thornton of York, 1941.

**61. Chair,** one of two, English, circa 1760-65
Mahogany with upholstered seat
H.37½ (95), W.24 (61), D.24 (61)

These chairs are closely related to a design by
Chippendale in his *Director* (1st edn., 1754, pl.XII and
3rd edn., 1762, pl.XIV). The drop-in seat is supported
by rebates on three sides of the seat rail and the frame
is strengthened by the use of pegged joints and
quadrant blocks.

The cabriole legs are carved at the knee with a double
cabochon motif and they stand on boldly scrolled toes.

PROV: Mallett, 1937.
CF.: A set of 11 chairs and a triple chair back settee formerly in the
Collection of Major E. A. Burnell-Milnes, Winkburn Hall, Newark, sold
by Sotheby's, March 10, 1933, lot 178, have a similar construction with
only minor variations in the carved detail. (Ill. C. Claxton Stevens and
S. Whittington, *The Norman Adams Collection,* 1983, p.48).
Further examples based on the same design are illustrated in Christopher
Gilbert, *The Life and Work of Thomas Chippendale,* 1978, vol.2, p.83,
f.131, in P. Macquoid and R. Edwards, *The Dictionary of English Furniture,*
rev. edn., 1954, p.278, f.164, (now in the Victoria and Albert Museum,
W.46-1926) and in P. Macquoid, *A History of English Furniture,* 1923,
vol.3, f.183.

# Chair

**62.  Chair,** one of eight and one armchair.
English, circa 1760-70
Mahogany with upholstered seat
H.38 (96), W.23 (58), D.23 (58)

Commonly referred to as 'ladderback' chairs, having
horizontal cross rails, waved to follow the line of the
cresting rail and decorated with pierced, interlacing
centres. The term is normally associated with a design
popularized during the middle part of the 18th century
by north country craftsmen. It is clear, however, that
these designs were often adapted and elaborated by the
London chairmakers, although no designs for such
appear in the *Director*[7] or were illustrated by Ince and
Mayhew[18]. Most of the set have replacement rails and
brackets, and the wide curved seats are supported by
filleted straight legs and linking stretchers.

The armchair has more elaborate interlacing on the
cross rails and the inward curving arms have inswept
supports carved with fluting and foliage on the
knuckle. A curved drop-in seat is supported on a plain
frame, strengthened by the use of quadrant blocks.

PROV: Mallett, 1937.

**63. Chair,** one of three, English, circa 1760
Mahogany; beech; with upholstered seat
H.38 (97), W.22 (56), D.18 (46)

The chairs are excellent examples of where the rococo, gothic and Chinese tastes are successfully combined, typifying a popular mid 18th century amalgamation.

The back has a waisted splat composed primarily of strapwork, interlaced with foliate scrolls and pendants, all framed between a pair of stop-fluted stiles and a delicately carved and crested top rail.

Wrap-over seats are fringed on the rail with inter-laced gothic tracery, whilst the spandrel brackets and legs are decorated with designs based on actual Chinese forms.

PROV: Mallett, 1936.
EXHIB: Temple Newsam, Leeds, *Thomas Chippendale,* 1951, no.111.
CF.: A single chair in the Collection of Stephen Winkworth, Esq., Craven Hill Gardens, London W1, was sold at Sotheby's on April 29, 1933. lot 777.
A set of six chairs now on display in the Wallace gallery of English Furniture at Colonial Williamsburg and formerly in the Collection of Mrs A. M. Montague, were sold at Christie's on June 8, 1967, lot 53.
Detailed comparison would suggest that all these chairs had formed part of a set.

# Armchair

**64.  Armchair,** English, circa 1760-70
Mahogany with upholstered seat and back
H.40 (102), W.28½ (73), D.32 (81)

The short cabriole legs at the front are carved at the knee with leaf and scroll decoration and they stand on scrolled toes. The splayed arms are also embellished with a cabochon and leaf motif and have been strengthened by steel brackets.

PROV: Charles Thornton of York, 1939.

**65.  Chair,** one of two, English, circa 1770-80
Mahogany with leather seat
H.37½ (95), W.21 (53), D.20 (51)

The backs are decorated in the gothic taste and the seats are supported by plain rails, legs and stretchers, with each principal joint being secured by the use of a single peg.

Fashions were changing at a mercurial pace during the middle of the 18th century and the gothic taste had been all but superseded by that of the Chinese taste,

although various gothic motifs were often used as part of other designs.

A few champions of the gothic, like the author and critic Horace Walpole, persisted in their support of this style, despite being severely criticised by friends as seeming to be 'unfashionable and middle class...'

In the provinces the need for change was less urgent and local cabinet-makers were producing work often 20 or 30 years behind the times.

PROV: Charles Thornton of York, 1932.

# Chair

**66. Chair,** one of two, English, circa 1780-85
Mahogany with solid seat
H.38 (97), W.21 (54), D.20½ (52)

The backs have curved cresting rails and pierced inter-lacing splats reminiscent of designs for chair backs shown in the 3rd edition of the *Director*.

**67. Settee,** English, circa 1780-90
Mahogany with upholstered back, seat and sides
H.37 (94), W.82 (208), D.35 (89)

A late 18th century settee, upholstered in a modern red cotton damask. The seat has been adapted to take coil springs at some time and examination of nail holes in the frame would suggest that this is the fourth or fifth re-covering.

It was a common practice in the mid 18th century for settees and chairs to be upholstered in the same fabric as the wall hangings, for the edges to be finished off with welting and then 'garnished' with brass nails. Single or double lines of nails were the usual treatment, but occasionally, as seen in the designs of Ince and Mayhew[18], the nails were arranged in decorative patterns around the edge.

The paintings of John Singleton Copley (1738-1815) show such sofas or settees having large cushions to the seat and on the back, whilst designs by Hepplewhite and Sheraton often show them fitted with bolsters at each end.

PROV: Charles Thornton of York, 1936.

# Chair

**68.  Armchair,** English, circa 1780-85
Mahogany with upholstered seat
H.37 (94), W.23 (58), D.20 (51)

The shield-shaped back has a pronounced concave curve
and is filled with slender, rising ribs which finish in
gathered leaf clusters.

Arm supports spring from the cappings of the two
front legs and they sweep backwards with rapid curves.

A guilloché moulding has been carved on all the
major surfaces and the tapered front legs are decorated
with rosettes and reeding. Underneath, corner brackets

have been added for extra strength and there are several
threaded holes, used when the frame has been screwed
to cross battens in the packing case during transit.

This type of chair is commonly associated with the
name of George Hepplewhite, who published his
*Cabinet-maker and Upholsterers' Guide* in 1788.

PROV: Francis Mallett, Esq., 1924.
     J. Rochelle Thomas, 1928 (a set of eight).
     Mallett, 1950.
EXHIB: Grafton Galleries, *Art Treasures Exhibition,* 1928, no.167.
LIT: P. Macquoid and R. Edwards, *The Dictionary of English Furniture,* 1st
edn., 1924, vol.I, p.253, f.142 and rev. edn., 1954, p.294, f.218.

**69.  Chair,** one of six, English, circa 1780-90
Mahogany with upholstered seat
H.36½ (93), W.20½ (52), D.20 (51)

This type of chair is popularly associated with the name of Hepplewhite but in fact has little or no connection with the designs in his *Guide.* It does, however, display a strong neo-classical influence and the severe but graceful outline is in marked contrast to the extravagant embellishments of the rococo taste.

The waisted splat has been pierced to resemble a wheatsheaf and the top-rail is carved with gathered ears of corn and trailing husk pendants at the corners. This type of drop-in seat was very popular towards the end of the eighteenth century, being supported on rebates in the seat rail whilst extra strength is provided by the use of quadrant blocks. The tapering front legs have been filleted at the front, to break up the rather stark line presented by the leading face and the plain stretchers have a typical English arrangement, linking all the legs together.

PROV: Charles Thornton of York, 1930.

# Chest of Drawers

**70.  Chest of Drawers,** English, circa 1705
Walnut; pine; oak
H.29½ (75), W.29 (73), D.14½ (37)

These pieces are popularly referred to as 'Bachelor's Chests', although this description is very much a 20th century convention. The front is fitted with three long drawers and two short dummy drawers all having their original brass handles and escutcheons.

When the folding top is opened out for writing and supported on the two slides, it would be difficult to use the drawers directly below if they could be pulled out at the front and they are therefore made to draw out at the sides being fitted out for ink-pots and quills.

PROV: J. McDowell, Esq., Sotheby's, Mar. 6, 1936, lot 143. Mallett, 1951.

**71. Press,** English, circa 1750
Mahogany; oak; pine
H.85 (216), W.53 (135), D.26½ (67)

The fielded door panels enclose a series of sliding trays
and the insides of the doors have been cut to continue
the rebate, so that the trays may be supported when
drawn forward to receive the folded clothes.

PROV: Sir Stuart Samuel, Chelwood Vetchery, Sussex.
R. A. Lee, circa 1930.
Hotspur, 1977.
ILL: M. Harris, *Old Furniture and Works of Decorative Art,* 1946, part II,
p.196.
LIT: *Connoisseur,* August, 1926.
CF.: P. Macquoid and R. Edwards, *The Dictionary of English Furniture,* rev.
edn., 1954, vol. II, p.167, f.17 (an example from the Percival Griffiths
Collection) and another in the Monro Collection sold at Christie's on June
27, 1985, lot 38.

# Chest of Drawers

**72. Chest of drawers,** English, circa 1760
Mahogany; pine; oak
H.34 (86), W.40 (102), D.21 (53)

The serpentine-front is fitted with four long drawers
below a narrow felt-covered slide that pulls out for use
when dressing. The corners are decorated with
representations of cluster columns and the drawers have
been fitted with replacement water-gilt brass handles
fashioned in the rococo taste.

The chest stands on shaped bracket feet strengthened
by the use of quadrant blocks on the inside.

PROV: J. C. Ionides, Esq., Hove, Sussex.
Mallett, 1934.
CF.: A second chest, the property of Mrs. Daphne Ionides was sold at
Christie's on May 4, 1950, lot 81 and is probably a pair to this chest.

**73. Chest of drawers,** English, circa 1760
Mahogany; pine; oak
H.34 (86), W.41½ (105), D.23½ (60)

The four long graduated drawers are housed below a waisted top, richly decorated at the edge with cabochon and scroll moulding. Corner pilasters are faced with carved consoles, foliage and rosettes on a ribbed ground, whilst the front sides are decorated with rosettes and diamond strapwork.

A carved carcass is supported on richly carved bracket feet fashioned in the Chinese taste.

PROV: Ernest Raphael, Esq., Sotheby's, Nov.9, 1945, lot 168. Mallett, 1945.
EXHIB: Temple Newsam, Leeds, *Thomas Chippendale,* 1951, no.105. Cannon Hall, Barnsley, *Chippendale Furniture,* 1963, no.37.

# Chest of Drawers

**74.  Chest of drawers,** English, circa 1765
Mahogany; oak; pine
H.37½ (95), W.45½ (115), D.22½ (57)

A finely grained mahogany serpentine-fronted chest of drawers, with five graduated drawers finished with their original brass handles in the rococo taste.

The canted corners are decorated with trailing leaves and husks and the panelled bracket feet are strengthened internally by the use of quadrant blocks, whilst brass and leather castors are provided to aid movement of the piece.

PROV: Sir Denzil Cope, Bt., Bramshill Park, Hampshire, Christie's, June 21, 1934, lot 126.

NOTE: Bramshill Park, a brick built mansion with stone dressings in the style of Hatfield House and Temple Newsam, was commissioned by Lord Zouch and completed externally in 1612. The house changed hands several times during the 17th century and was bought in 1700 by Sir John Cope, Bt., in whose family possession it remained until 1934. Early photographs of the interiors *(Country Life,* vol.5, April 8, 1899, p.432-5 and vol.14, July 11, 1903, p.54-8) show rooms filled with an impressive array of English furniture. Many take their inspiration from designs by Robert Manwaring (A. Coleridge, *Chippendale Furniture,* 1968, f.132-3) and John Linnell (R. Edwards and M. Jourdain, *Georgian Cabinet-makers,* 1944, p.78) and are illustrated in P. Macquoid and R. Edwards, *The Dictionary of English Furniture,* 1st edn., 1924 and rev.edn., 1954.

**75. Chest of drawers,** English, circa 1760
Mahogany; pine; oak
H.35 (89), W.38 (97), D.19 (48)

A serpentine-fronted mahogany chest of drawers, having canted corners carved in the Chinese taste and standing on shaped ogee feet. The four graduated drawers are lined with oak throughout and the fronts are edged with a delicate corded inlay.

PROV: Charles Thornton of York, 1947.

# Chest of Drawers

**76.** **Chest of drawers,** English
Mahogany; pine; oak
H.33 (81), W.33 (81), D.19 (49)

This serpentine-fronted mahogany chest of drawers is of similar design to a 'French Commode Table' illustrated in Thomas Chippendale, *The Gentleman & Cabinet-maker's Director*, 1754, pl. XLV.

The top drawer is fitted out as a dressing slide with an adjustable mirror and compartments for bottles and combs, whilst below there is an unusual arrangement of a further one long and two short drawers.

The scrolled legs at the front form part of the construction, whilst the rear legs join the carcass at its base.

PROV: R. A. Lee, circa 1948.

**77. Dressing chest,** possibly Irish, circa 1770
Mahogany; oak; pine
H.34 (87), W.34 (86), D.23 (59)

A combined writing and dressing chest veneered in Cuban mahogany.

The pilasters, decorated with acanthus and open leaf carving, slide out with the top drawer to create a working surface with trays and containers at the sides for quills and inkpots, and in addition, the writing top slides back to give access below.

The drawers are fitted with replacement handles and the top lifts up to reveal a dressing glass and compartments intended for bottles, combs, etc.

PROV: Charles Thornton of York, 1930.

# Chest of Drawers

A design for a French commode table of bombé form, illustrated in the first edition of Chippendale's *Director* (1754), pl.XLIII.

The term 'bombé' is of French origin and is used to describe furniture which has a swelling outline towards the base as in the case of typical Dutch furniture. The term has been used, however, to describe other pieces with similar swellings but not necessarily at the base.

**78.  Chest of drawers,** English, circa 1760
Mahogany; pine; oak
H.35 (89), W.48½ (123), D.23 (59)

This mahogany 'commode', of bombé form is closely related to Chippendale's design and the slight variations that can be observed typify the problems that craftsmen have when trying to 'work out' the design in wood.

This bombé shape is extremely difficult to fashion, having three dimensional curves which not only affect the external appearance, but also increase the complexity of the joints.

PROV: The Earl of Dartmouth, Sotheby's, Oct. 31, 1947, lot 181.
    Mallett, 1947.
EXHIB: Temple Newsam, Leeds, *Thomas Chippendale,* 1951, no.106.

# Dressing Commode

A design for a lady's dressing table published in the 3rd edition of Chippendale's *Director* (1762), pl.LII.

He comments in the complementary notes that 'the drawer above the recess hath all conveniences for dressing, and the top of it is a dressing glass which comes forward with folding hinges. On each side is a cupboard, with glass doors which may be either transparent or silvered and on the inside drawers or pigeon holes'. Chippendale also mentions that two such dressing tables have been made of rosewood from this design and that they give 'entire satisfaction'. A dressing table of similar design, made in rosewood for Lady Arniston of Arniston House in Midlothian is now part of the Leverhulme Collection at the Lady Lever Art Gallery, Port Sunlight. (C. Gilbert, *The Life and Work of Thomas Chippendale*, 1978, vol.2, p.227, f.414, also illustrated in A. Coleridge, *Chippendale Furniture*, 1968, f.165.)

**81.  Dressing Commode,** English, circa 1760
Mahogany; pine; oak
H.60 (153), W.46½ (118), D.25 (64)

The shaped front with its kneehole recess, has an
elaborately fitted out top drawer, whilst in the upper
section there is a central pivoting mirror set within a
rococo frame which had been fitted on to extending
hinged brackets at some time.

PROV: The Dukes of Manchester, Kimbolton Castle, Huntingdon.
Knight, Frank and Rutley, July 18-21, 1949, lot 364.
Walter P. Chrysler, Jnr., Parke-Bernet Galleries, New York, May
6, 1960.
Hotspur, 1976.
EXHIB: Temple Newsam, Leeds, *Thomas Chippendale,* 1951, no. 81.
LIT: F. Lenygon, *Furniture in England 1660-1760,* 1922, p.173, f.258.
P. Macquoid and R. Edwards, *The Dictionary of English Furniture,* 1st edn.,
1927, vol.III, p.219, f.13.
M. Jourdain and R. Edwards, *Georgian Cabinet-makers,* 1955, f.97.
R. W. Symonds, *Antique Collector,* June, 1955, p.118.

# Tallboy Secretaire

**82. Tallboy secretaire,** English, circa 1765
Mahogany; pine; oak
H.69 (176), W.51 (130, D.24½ (62)

Constructed in two sections and having canted corners, enriched with fluted columns and panelled bases.

The bottom drawer of the top section pulls out to form a secretaire and the working height of the fall front suggests that it was intended for use whilst standing. This type of tallboy is usually thought to have a north country origin.

PROV: Charles Thornton of York, 1928.

**83.  Chest of drawers,** English, circa 1770
Mahogany; satinwood; pine; oak
H.34 (87), W.44 (112), D.24 (61)

The veneered top has oval mahogany medallions set within a field of satinwood, a timber also used to form the herringbone pattern on the canted corners and to edge the drawer fronts.

Within the carcass are four long drawers and the top one has been elaborately fitted out for dressing with a central adjustable mirror with its original silvered glass plate and various compartments for boxes, brushes, combs and bottles etc.

Satinwood became increasingly popular during the 18th century and was used as a veneer on furniture from about 1760 onwards. It was shipped in from Guiana in the West Indies and used sparingly in solid form because of the expense. The timber was also being brought in from the East Indies and although considered inferior, was used extensively until its place was taken by rosewood during the early 1800's.

PROV: Mallett, 1945.

# Chest of Drawers

**84. Chest of drawers,** English, circa 1775
Mahogany; oak; pine
H.34 (87), W.46 (117), D.24½ (62)

A mahogany serpentine-fronted chest of drawers, with four plain graduated drawers set between canted corners decorated with fluting and fitted with water-gilt brass drop handles.

PROV: Mallett, 1932.

**85.  Chest of drawers,** English, circa 1785
Mahogany; oak; pine
H.32 (82), W.41½ (105), D.19½ (50)

A mahogany serpentine-fronted chest of drawers with
four plain graduated drawers fitted with simple brass
drop handles, set within a plain carcass frame and
standing on shaped bracket feet.

PROV: Mallett, 1929.

# Chest of Drawers

**86.   Chest of drawers,** English, circa 1790
Mahogany; pine
H.31 (79), W.35½ (90), D.17½ (45)

A small mahogany serpentine-fronted chest of drawers standing on simple bracket feet and having four graduated drawers decorated with fine banded inlay, set within canted corners inlaid to represent fluting.

PROV: Mallett, 1935.

**87. Chest of drawers,** English, circa 1795
Pine
H.32½ (82), W.80½ (205), D.19 (48)

A japanned dwarf chest of drawers, having a central recessed cupboard with two panelled doors, surrounded by a series of nine drawers that are lined with their original fabric.

The designs in the lacquer work display a delightful naivety of execution and may well be the result of some English amateur artist who, having obtained the plain pine carcass, set about decorating it, using contemporary publications such as Robert Sayers' *Ladies Amusement or Whole Art of Japanning made Easy* as a guide. This decoration has been carried out using paint and varnish applied straight on to the pine carcass, whereas the japanning techniques employed at the beginning of the 18th century involved a much more elaborate preparation of the surface first. It would have been coated with many layers of sizing or 'whiting' that had been allowed to dry properly between each layer, then polished and varnished until the surface glistened like a mirror. A mixture of sizing and gum was painted onto the surface to the designs required and this formed the basis for the application of speckles of gold dust and other metal powders dropped from a sprinkler.

PROV: V., 1927 (identity unknown).

# Cistern Stand

**88.  Cistern stand,** English, circa 1810
Mahogany; bronze
H.40 (102), W.15 (39), D.15 (39)

A bronze and mahogany washing stand, fashioned in the Egyptian style with a fluted shaft rising from a triple sphinx base that supports a waisted bowl decorated with gadrooning. Fitted on the rim, are three shaped scallop-shell soap holders with overflow holes linked to the interior. A small screw thread fitment on the underside of the bowl allows water to be pumped into the bowl, and this then drains away down the shaft into a metal cistern housed within the base. The container, with its small hinged handle, can hold approximately three pints of water and would presumably need emptying after each meal. Three scrolled legs are decorated with a rising acanthus leaf and are fitted with bronze feet shaped to represent the paws of the Chimera, a fire-breathing monster with a lion's head found in Greek mythology.

The Egyptian taste is a term given to a short lived attempt to introduce the shapes, symbols and forms of ancient Egypt into furniture dating from about 1790-1820. It was fuelled very much by Napoleon's Egyptian campaign of 1798 and by the work of the artist Denon, who accompanied the armies on their expedition. His extremely popular illustrated volume *Voyage dans la Haute et dans la Basse Egypte,* provided a wealth of ideas for designers both in France and in England. Thomas Hope (1769-1831), the wealthy architect and author, was considered the leading English exponent of this style and his designs for furniture and dining pieces were also based on motifs taken from Egyptian idols, bas reliefs and plates in the *Herculaneum Collection,* Sheraton's publication a few years earlier.

Washing stands had become very popular by the early part of the 19th century and were considered very fashionable for Bedrooms, Drawing rooms and Dining rooms. They were normally constructed in wood and often designed to fit into a corner or recess with a curtain or shutter to disguise their purpose. This example is most unusual however, with its combination of bronze and mahogany.

PROV: Albert Amor, circa 1930.
     R. A. Lee, 1932.
     Mallett, 1935.

**89.  Commode cupboard,** English, circa 1765
Mahogany; pine; oak
H.32 (81), W.29½ (75), D.21 (54)

The bracket feet, canted corners and frieze have been decorated with applied fretwork in the Chinese taste and carrying handles are fitted to the sides. A single sliding drawer originally housing a chamber pot, has been adapted to create the present arrangement below and the two drawers have replacement handles.

PROV: Ernest Raphael, Esq., Sotheby's, Nov. 9, 1945, lot 152.
    Mallett, 1945.
EXHIB: Temple Newsam, Leeds, *Thomas Chippendale,* 1951, no. 108.

# Dressing Glass

**90.  Dressing glass,** English, circa 1700
Walnut; oak
H.37 (64), W.18 (45), D.10½ (27)

The stand is fashioned to represent a miniature of
contemporary bureaux and is fitted out with a long
serpentine-fronted drawer containing boxes and
compartments, whilst the fall front drops to reveal the
usual arrangement of drawers and pigeon-holes.

These pieces were normally placed on small stands or
dressing tables and as the century advanced became
incorporated within the overall design.

PROV: Charles Thornton of York, 1938.

**91. Dressing glass,** English, circa 1800
Mahogany
H.24½ (63), W.22½ (57), D.10 (26)

Throughout the 18th century, the dressing glass, or toilet mirror continued to have its place in the arrangement of the closet. By the end of the century, the stand was no longer elaborately fitted out, and had usually taken on this more skeletonised form.

PROV: Rev. R. Holden, Nuthall Temple, Notts.
    Charles Thornton of York, 1928.
NOTE: Stephen Wright's Nuthall Temple was, like Chiswick, a copy of Palladio's Villa Almerico (usually referred to as the Villa Rotunda) at Vicenza. The house was destroyed by fire in 1929.

# Linen Press

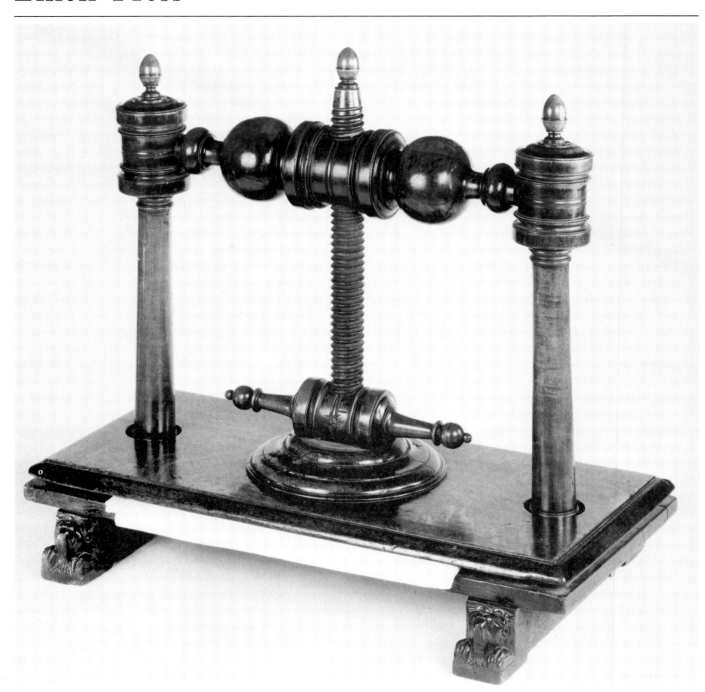

**92.  Linen press,** English, circa 1690
Walnut; oak
H.25 (64), W.28 (71), D.17 (44)

The piece has a turned walnut frame and oak press boards which stand on blocks fashioned to represent a seated lion. A spiral screw is used to raise or lower the top board and the linen or damask is folded and placed between the boards for pressing.

Dutch paintings of the late 17th century, occasionally show walls lined with hangings that appear to have a large check pattern. This is now thought to be fold lines caused by the linen press.

PROV: D. M. Weatherley, Esq.
Charles Thornton of York, 1940.

**93. Mirror,** English, circa 1710
Pine; gesso. H.52½ (133), W.28½ (72)

The mirror is fitted with a replacement bevelled glass
housed in a gesso frame which is decorated in the
cresting with a female mask surrounded by scrolling

leaves, gadrooning and turned eagles' heads.

PROV: Charles Davis, Esq., 1908.
   Mrs. George Eumorfopoulos, Sotheby's, Feb. 28, 1944, lot 50.
   Mallett, 1944.
EXHIB: Shepherd's Bush, London, *Franco-British Exhibition,* May 14, 1908,
no.1095.

# Plate Buckets

**94. Plate buckets,** English, circa 1800
Mahogany; brass
H.17 (43), Diam.14½ (37)

Both buckets are carved with diagonal reeding, but
only one has been fitted with a door at the side.

Because of the long distance that usually separated
the Kitchen from the Dining room such pails proved
invaluable, not only for transportation but to keep the
plates warm at the table.

PROV: Charles Thornton of York, 1938.

**95.  Secretaire,** English, circa 1760
Mahogany; pine; oak
H.69 (175), W.28 (71), D.13 (33)

The pierced shelving above is fashioned in the gothic taste and intended for the display of china, whilst below, the lower section has four long drawers and a fall front secretaire fitted with the usual arrangement of small drawers and pigeon-holes.

PROV: Mrs. J. A. Turner, West Downs, Petersfield.
Hotspur, 1963.

# Secretaire

**96.  Secretaire,** English, circa 1760
attributed to the workshops of William Vile
Mahogany; oak; pine
H.71½ (182), W.24½ (62), D.12½ (32)

The latticework superstructure on the two upper
sections is of unusual intricacy and the decorated friezes
that separate the sections have secret slides which pull
out at the front.

A fall front writing board is supported on brass
quadrants housed within the carcass and the interior is
fitted with drawers and pigeon-holes, constructed
throughout of mahogany. The legs are decorated with
trailing pendants of leaf and flower on the leading edges
and are strengthened by the application of scrolled
spandrel brackets.

The fretwork is constructed using a laminate of
mahogany. Three thin layers are glued together so that
when the material is subjected to variations in
temperature and humidity, the laminate can expand and
contract without detriment to the structure.

Doors in the top section are held fast by an ingenious
device that secures both by a single action. When the
key is used, bolts are in turn activated in the other
door, thus locking them in place.

In addition, the two secret slides below are secured
by the use of springloaded latch bolts. Narrow beading
is used to embellish the joints and edges of these
sections and this decoration is often seen on work
attributed to the workshops of Vile. Similarly the
elegant waved pattern, usually referred to as a
Vitruvian scroll and applied to the frieze, is another
favoured motif.

The cast brass water-gilt handles are also strikingly
similar to the fitments found on several tables and
commodes attributed to this craftsman.

PROV: Lady Dudley Ward.
       Mallett, 1964.
EXHIB: Victoria and Albert Museum, London, *B.A.D.A. Golden Jubilee
Exhibition,* 1968, no.140.
LIT: *Burlington Magazine,* December, 1920.
CF.: An almost identical cabinet, differing only in minor details of carving,
is illustrated in P. Macquoid and R. Edwards, *The Dictionary of English
Furniture,* rev. edn., 1954, vol.I, p.151, f.58. Both this and the Terry
cabinet relate to the celebrated 'Secretary' supplied to Queen Charlotte by
Vile in 1761 for the sum of £71.10s.0d.

Each pierced panel is held within the frame by the use of delicate carved beading.

William Vile joined in partnership with an upholsterer named John Cobb to work in London from about 1750. It would seem that Vile was the dominant partner, he being the one who was appointed to the post of 'Cabinet-maker to the Royal Household', an honour not given to John Cobb when Vile disappeared from the scene in 1765.

Royal patronage had come late to the firm, but following the accession of King George III and Queen Charlotte to the throne in 1761, there was a spate of important commissions. They supplied the Royal Household with writing tables, jewel cabinets, bookcases and an organ case in addition to the secretaire previously mentioned and this definitely had a healthy effect on the bank balance. It is interesting to note that by 1762, William Vile had amassed £3,728 in his account[2].

During this period covering the first decade of George III's reign, pride of place amongst the contemporary cabinet-makers must be assigned to William Vile and his workshop. Other famous names

such as William Hallett, John Bradburn and William France were associated with the firm either financially or physically and many of the pieces produced are likely to be the combined efforts of a group of craftsmen.

The other partner, John Cobb, was most remembered for his 'singularly haughty manner' and described as 'one of the proudest men in England'. He was frequently observed strutting through the workshop giving orders to his men and even reprimanded by George III on one occasion in the Library of Buckingham Palace for his unhelpful manner.

Reference to the two partners in contemporary invoices assign the title of 'Upholder' to John Cobb and 'Cabinet-maker' to Vile, but it is unlikely that these definitions and specialities persisted, although they would have brought their own skills and talents to bear in the supervision of the workmen. Cobb's name is usually associated with some fine marquetry furniture, and a satinwood commode and pair of vase stands were supplied by Cobb in 1772 to Paul Methuen of Corsham Court, Wiltshire.

The legs are chamfered on the inside and stand on recessed brass and leather castors.

# Sideboard

**97.  Sideboard,** English, circa 1810
Mahogany; pine
H.35 (88), W.75 (190), D.31 (79)

The brass rail at the back is normally hung with silk to prevent splashes from marking the wall and the two deep drawers on the front, with their inlaid shield motifs, were originally both sliding, but one has been converted to a cupboard and fitted inside with shelves. On one side, a small cupboard has been incorporated to house a chamber pot which was intended for the convenience of the gentlemen, once the ladies had retired to the Drawing room.

PROV: Charles Thornton of York, 1947.

**98.  Spinet,** English, July 17th, 1769
John Kirsham of Manchester (active 1740-1773)
Walnut; pine; mahogany
H.34½ (88), L.76½ (194), D.28½ (72)

The veneered walnut case is crossbanded and inlaid with boxwood stringing, whilst the top and lid are made in solid mahogany with an external hook and hinges. A walnut tripod stand, with slender cabriole legs, has a small drawer incorporated in the front of the frame. The keyboard has a range of 4½ octaves, from FF to GG-f³ and the keys have ivory 'naturals' with arcaded fronts, together with ebony 'accidentals'. The date of manufacture is recorded on the bottom key, whilst the top key has been used by Charles Thornton, to record his sale to Noel Terry. Apparently Kirsham is the only known Manchester maker of this period and his work is documented between 1740 and 1773. There are seven other instruments known to have been made by him of which three have similar characteristics.

PROV: Charles Thornton of York, 1928.

# Writing Table

**99. Writing table,** English, circa 1690
Walnut; oak
H.27 (69), W.31½ (80), D.12½ (32)

Tables specifically designed for writing at do not seem to have been made in England until the end of the 17th century, in marked contrast to the Continent, where carefully thought out arrangements for such an activity were prevalent over a century before.

This example is typical of these early English pieces, being rectangular in form and having a folding top, decorated with a parquetry inlay arranged in a geometric pattern and having two legs which swing out to give support. Within the top are shallow compartments for documents and to the side are drawers, fitted out for quills and ink pots.

PROV: Mallett, 1933.
CF.: A writing table of similar form but nearly twice the length in the Long Gallery at Boughton House, Northamptonshire.

**100. Table,** English, circa 1730
Walnut; pine; oak
H.28½ (72), W.42 (107), D.22 (56)

A serpentine-fronted dressing or writing table, veneered in walnut with boxwood and ebony banding on both the top and the sides.

The kneehole front has three drawers, plus a further two that pull out at the sides. Hidden within the side frames are two secret compartments, ingeniously held in place by the side drawer runners and access to these compartments can only be gained by the complete removal of both side and front drawers. The runners then lift up and finger recesses underneath permit the sealed oak boxes to be pushed out.

Four boldly carved cabriole legs are decorated with scrolled foliage and trailing husks and whilst the two rear legs have been left plain at the back, all the feet are richly carved with a hairy paw and ball.

PROV: C. Fredricks.
    R. A. Lee.
    Mallett, 1949.
EXHIB: Grosvenor House, Antique Dealers Fair, 1949.

# Gate-leg Table

**101.  Gate-leg table,** English, circa 1730
Mahogany; pine
H.28 (71), W.ext.62½ (159), D.46 (117)

The piece stands on straight legs with claw and ball feet and two of the legs pivot out, giving support to the hinged flaps.

Specific rooms intended for eating or dining in were still something of a novelty at the beginning of the 18th century and it was usual to have two or more of these tables set up in the same room. The table manners of the English gentry were always a good topic of conversation for those on the Continent and visitors to this country were often amazed at how primitive the eating arrangements were. Our custom of eating plain unfancy food, hardly ever using forks and smoking tobacco at the table after the meal, was guaranteed to send a shiver down the spine of many a fashionable French gourmet.

PROV: Albert Amor, 1926.

# Artist's Table

**102. Artist's table,** English, circa 1755
Mahogany. H.28½ (72), W.25 (64), D.19 (48)

During the 18th century, such tables were seen as 'very healthy for those who stand to read, write or draw' and Arthur Devis illustrated this type of table being used by the Reverend Edward Hoyle in 1760. The table combines the gothic and Chinese tastes in its decoration. Pierced fretwork in the Chinese manner fills the frieze and the legs are formed as cluster columns, all strengthened by the use of pierced spandrel brackets.

A double rising top is worked by a ratchet concealed in the superstructure and a removable reading rail stows away underneath when not required.

PROV: Sir Sidney Greville.
R. A. Lee.
Mallett, 1934.
EXHIB: Temple Newsam, Leeds, *Thomas Chippendale,* 1951, no.107.
CF.: An almost identical piece is illustrated in P. Macquoid and R. Edwards, *The Dictionary of English Furniture,* 1st edn., 1927, vol.III, p.180, f.3.

# Tripod Table

**103.  Tripod table,** English, circa 1755
Mahogany. H.29 (74), W.24 (61)

A pierced gallery surrounds an octagonal shaped top joined to the column by a hinged fitment. This allows the top to be swung into the vertical position so that the table can be stored against the wall when not in use. The column and base are both formed from elaborately pierced and carved 'S' shaped scrolls and the scrolled toes are fitted with small brass and leather castors.

Towards the middle of the 18th century the tea gardens situated in and around London had become quite unsavoury places and the custom of taking tea in each other's houses soon became established.

Craftsmen, keen to capitalise on this new craze, began producing richly embellished tables specifically designed for this activity and the fashion soon spread to all levels of society.

PROV: Mallett, 1951.
CF.: A table with no provenance illustrated in the Furniture Department archives of the Victoria and Albert Museum (microfiche No.8146.)
NOTE: The shape of the column and tripod base has many similarities with designs illustrated in Ince and Mayhew's *Universal System of Household Furniture,* 1762, plates XIII, XIV and LIII.

# Tea Table

**104. Tea table,** probably Irish, circa 1760
Mahogany; pine
H.28½ (72), W.34 (87), D.22½ (57)

In addition to the occasional tea tables more likely intended for individual use, there were the larger Tea or China tables, decorated on all sides.

They are popularly referred to as 'centre tables', although it is unlikely that during the 18th century they would be left out in the centre of the room as a permanent feature.

This particular Cuban mahogany example has a tray top above an unusually deep frieze, decorated with a boldly carved gadrooned edge which centres on a shell motif. The four richly carved legs have an accentuated cabriole form decorated at the knee with rosettes and trailing acanthus leaf, whilst the claw and ball feet splay out with an unusual degree of exaggeration.

PROV: Mallett, 1935.
CF.: A table with no provenance illustrated in the Furniture Department archives of the Victoria and Albert Museum, (microfiche No.6488.)
NOTE: Attribution to the Irish school of craftsmen is not based on fact, but many of the unusual construction techniques employed are mirrored on known pieces from the Dublin school.

# Writing Table

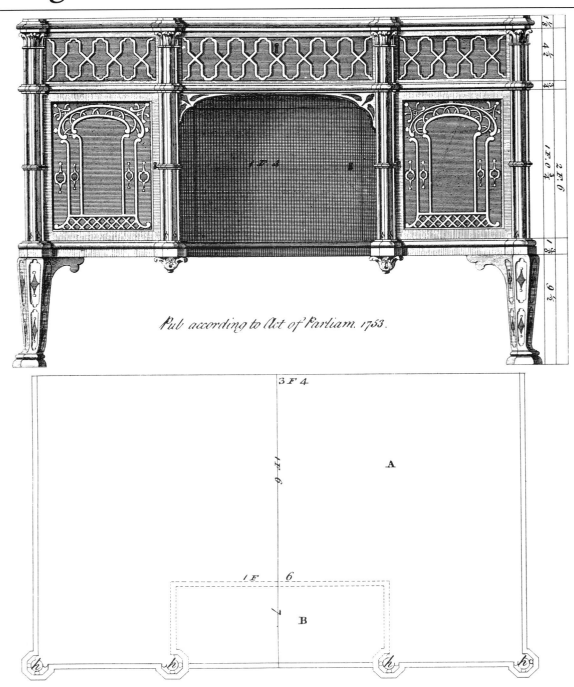

Pub according to Act of Parliam. 1753.

An illustration taken from Chippendale's 1st edition of the *Director* (1754), pl.LII, showing designs for a writing table in the gothic taste.

In his footnotes Chippendale specifies that it is to have 'one long drawer at the top, doors at each end, drawers in the inside and a recess for the knees as you see in plan B. The columns are fixed to the door(s) and open with them'. He gives drawings for the top, columns and mouldings and notes that 'this table has been made more than once from this design and has a better appearance when executed, than in the drawing'.

Considerable emphasis was being placed on designs for library tables during the middle of the 18th century. Chippendale had provided eleven designs in his third edition of the *Director* (1762), whilst Ince and Mayhew's *Universal System* (1762), showed three.

**105. Writing table,** English, circa 1755
after a design by Thomas Chippendale
Mahogany; pine; oak
H.30½ (78), W.45 (115), D.27 (68)

The long drawer at the top forms part of the frieze and pulls out to reveal a leather-covered writing surface which incorporates a hinged platform, designed to act as a reading stand. This writing surface in turn slides back to give access to various partitioned compartments and a hinged quadrant ink-well swings out at the side for use when the writing surface is in position.

The cluster columns are formed as part of the doors, opening with them and they have the rising flame decoration applied at the base of each column that corresponds to the details shown on Chippendale's drawing.

Minor variations from the original drawing include the absence of spandrel brackets in the kneehole recess. To include them would, of course, inhibit the opening and closing of the cupboard door.

A much simpler cluster column motif has also been used in the frieze and there are no pendant finials hanging from the columns. In addition, plain cabriole legs substitute for Chippendale's more elaborate pillar supports which are seen decorated with sunken panels.

PROV: Mallett, 1950.
EXHIB: Temple Newsam, Leeds, *Thomas Chippendale,* 1951, no.104.
LIT: P. Macquoid and R. Edwards, *The Dictionary of English Furniture,* rev. edn., 1954, vol.III, p.248, f.18.
M. Jourdain and R. Edwards, *Georgian Cabinet-makers,* rev. edn., 1955, f.103.
R. W. Symonds, *Antique Collector,* June, 1955, p.119.
A. Coleridge, *Chippendale Furniture,* 1968, f.244.
CF.: A writing table that corresponds in nearly every detail was sold at Christie's on 24 April, 1958, lot 69.

# Two-tier Table

**106.   Two-tier table,** English, circa 1755
Mahogany. H.37 (94), W.25 (64)

A two-tier mahogany dumb-waiter, with revolving octagonal tiers edged with a pierced gallery.

The tripod base corresponds to a design in the first edition of the *Director*[6] and the column is of baluster form, carved with acanthus and fluting.

A 1755 inventory taken at Chicheley Hall, Bucks records the presence of a "mahogany dumb-waiter in the Common Parlour" indicating that the description was a popular one from the outset.

PROV: Hotspur, 1954.
EXHIB: Victoria and Albert Museum, London, *International Art Treasures Exhibition*, 1962, no. 85.
LIT: A. Coleridge, *Chippendale Furniture*, 1968, f.227.

**107.   Tripod table,** English, circa 1760
Mahogany. H.42 (107), Diam.26½ (68)

The table has a circular top with a raised border, popularly referred to as a 'piecrust edge'. In the first half of the 18th century it was common for tea or coffee sets to be displayed on large silver salvers and simple wooden tripod stands were often made to support these trays. It seems likely that 18th century cabinet-makers decided to work this out fully in wood and it resulted in the development of occasional tables such as this. The top is shown tilted into the vertical position, allowing the table to be stored at the side of a room when not in use.

PROV: Mallett, 1932.

# Table

**108.  Table,** English, circa 1760
Mahogany. H.28 (71), W.33 (84), D.25 (64)

A mahogany centre table, with a shaped top, bowed to
front and back and supported by a frieze decorated with
carved leaf and cabochon motifs. The four cabriole legs
are richly embellished with acanthus leaves at the knee
and they continue with a trailing leaf stem down the
leg, towards the elegantly scrolled toes. The decorative
treatment of this table is reminiscent of designs shown
in Ince and Mayhew's *Universal System*[18].

PROV: Leidesdorf Collection, sold at Sotheby's, New York on June
27-28, 1974, lot 58.

**109.  Writing table,** English, circa 1760
Mahogany; oak; pine
H.32½ (82), W.55 (140), D.28 (71)

A kneehole writing table, with serpentine front and a central sliding cupboard set within an archivolt which is supported by fluted pilasters.

Around this cupboard are nine drawers, each fitted with water-gilt brass handles and escutcheon plates in the rococo taste. The canted corners have been embellished with garlands of fruit and flowers that trail from the scrolled consoles and the whole is mounted on inset castors, provided to aid movement of the piece.

PROV: Mrs. George Edwardes, Christie's, Dec. 6, 1934, lot 73. (The catalogue illustration shows only scrolled consoles on the canted corners. The garlands have been a later addition).
Charles Thornton of York, 1946.

CF.: A writing table illustrated in the Untermyer Collection Catalogue and a similar piece formerly at Hazelwood Castle, Yorks. sold by H. Spencer and Sons, June 15, 1972, lot 543.

A further example from the Mansion House, London, in the style of William Vile is illustrated in A. Coleridge, *Chippendale Furniture,* 1968, fig. 19.

# Table

**110.  Table,** English, circa 1760
Mahogany. H.29½ (75), W.32 (81), D.21 (54)

A tea or china table, elaborately decorated in the Chinese taste with pierced fretwork on the legs, frieze and gallery.

Plain turned legs are surrounded on two sides with fretted panels cut with a rolling leaf pattern and they stand on leather and brass castors.

There are similar patterns for frets illustrated in John Crunden's *The Joyner and Cabinet-maker's Darling,* 1765 which, although concentrating on architecture, also illustrates designs that were 'proper' for bookcases, tea-tables, trays and fenders.

PROV: Charles Thornton of York, 1935.

**111.  Table,** English, circa 1770
Mahogany. H.28 (72), W.ext.32 (81), D.32 (81)

A gateleg table, with slender turned spindle legs and
stretchers standing on peg feet. The 1776 inventory
taken at the Vyne in Hampshire describes this type as
a 'spider-leg' table and this is in fact the popular name
which is adopted today. It would be intended for use
in the Drawing room, rather than the Dining room.

PROV: Charles Thornton of York, 1931.

# Card Table

**112.   Card table,** one of two, English, circa 1765
Mahogany; pine; oak
H.29½ (75), W.39½ (100), D.19½ (50)

The pair are elegantly carved with serpentine fronts
and have shaped folding tops lined with green felt
on the inside. The legs are of slender cabriole form,
standing on scrolled toes and one leg pivots out at
the rear to give support to the opened top. Set
within the frame is a small drawer which has been
partitioned off to hold four packs of cards and this
is revealed when the table is arranged for gaming.

Card-playing during the first half of the 18th
century, stimulated by the speculative mania
prevalent at the time, took on such proportions
that the Sovereign, Queen Anne, found it necessary to place a heavy tax on the purchase of cards
and dice in an effort to discourage the game.

PROV: Lady Sinclair, Stevenson Hall, near Haddington, Edinburgh,
      Dowells, May 2, 1931.
      Charles Thornton of York, 1931.
CF.: A pair of card tables, supplied by Thomas Chippendale in 1759 to
the Earl of Dumfries for the Blue Drawing Room at Dumfries House,
Scotland. (C. Gilbert, *The Life and Work of Thomas Chippendale,* 1978,
vol.II, f.402-404).

**113.  Card table,** English, circa 1765-70
possibly by Joseph Ward of Margaret St., London
Mahogany; pine; oak
H.29½ (75), W.39 (99), D.19 (48)
Inventory mark 27237/575004/W shown on the inside
of one rear leg.

The serpentine front has a shaped frieze carved with
fluting that supports a folding gaming surface lined
with baize and enriched at the edges with a leaf pattern.
On top, there is a geometric marquetry design of
mahogany veneers, edged with boxwood banding.

The slender cabriole legs are extravagantly carved

and both legs at the rear pivot out and give support to
the opened lined playing surface.

PROV: Dukes of Northumberland, Albury Park, Surrey.
    B. & S. Dean Levy, New York, 1959.
    Hotspur, 1976.
CF.: A pair of stools with strikingly similar carved detail supplied by Ward
to Lord Langdale of Holme Hall, North Yorkshire in 1777, were sold at
Sotheby's, March 13, 1959, lot 34.
NOTE: 'A list of eminent Cabinet-makers, Inlayers and Upholders',
compiled by Lady Northumberland, apparently in 1776, shows the name
of Joseph Ward in competition with such firms as Vile and Cobb, Ince
and Mayhew, Chippendale and Linnell. (C. Gilbert, *The Life and Work
of Thomas Chippendale,* 1978, vol. I, p.153-4).

# Dining Table

**114.  Dining table,** English, circa 1775
Mahogany; pine; oak
H.29½ (75), L.ext.106(270), W.48 (122)

PROV: Charles Thornton of York, 1933.
CF.: A dining table with no provenance, illustrated in the Furniture Department archives of the Victoria and Albert Museum, London, (microfiche No.9671.)

A mahogany drop-leaf dining table (not illustrated) with two semi-circular 'D' ends. These detachable 'D' ends stand in a pier when not in use, and the friezes are elaborately carved with baskets of grapes, linked together with swagged garlands of fruit. The completed table cannot be used in the traditional English way, with the host sitting at the head, but will allow the guests and the host to take up a less formal arrangement in the manner of the French.

**115. Quartetto tables,** English, circa 1790
Beechwood; amboyna
H.30½ (78), W.17 (44), D.11½ (29)

A set of small tables, graduated to fit one below another with narrow turned beechwood legs, supporting finely marked amboyna tops.

Sheraton in his *Cabinet Dictionary,* 1803, suggests that this type of table could be used for needlework whilst George Smith's *Household Furniture,* 1808, assigns them to Drawing rooms where they 'prevent the company rising from their seats when taking refreshments'.

# Games Table

**116.   Games table,** possibly Indonesian, circa 1800
Sabicu; satinwood; mahogany
H.30 (76), W.ext.42 (107), D.22 (56)

A games-table of sofa table form, with sliding
reversible panel and hinged side flaps. The interior is
fitted out with a backgammon board and has a set of
carved ivory 'tables' or counters decorated with Chinese
scenes. The reversible top can be used for chess and
there is a shallow sliding drawer fitted below.

Before the introduction of cards in the 15th century,
the most popular games of chance were those of backgammon and chess, games known in England since
before the Norman conquest. Proficiency at these was
considered a 'polite accomplishment' for fashionable
young men and women of the Georgian era.

PROV: Charles Thornton of York, 1947.
NOTE: Whilst the quality of this table is better than would be expected
of an Indonesian piece, a Far Eastern source seems likely, given the
unusual construction and jointing techniques used.

**117. Tea table,** English, circa 1815
Mahogany. H.28 (72), Diam.15 (38)

An occasional mahogany tea table carved with reeding
on the column and stand. The circular tray top has two
slides below, which can be pulled out to provide
support for the cups and saucers.

# Sofa Table

**118.  Sofa table,** English, circa 1815
Mahogany; pine; coromandel
H.29 (73), W.ext.62½ (159), D.27½ (70)

A veneered sofa table, with two large end flaps
supported on hinged brackets at the sides. Below the
top, which is edged with coromandel-wood, there are
two real and two dummy drawers lined with
cedarwood and fitted with brass scallop-shell handles.
The stands are decorated with a simple inlay of ebony
and are linked together by a turned stretcher, whilst the
outward curving legs are fitted with brass lion's head
caps and castors.

# Sofa Table

**119.   Sofa table,** English, circa 1820
Rosewood; pine; oak
H.29 (74), W.ext.59½ (151), D.28 (71)

A sofa table, with hinged side flaps supported on brackets that pivot out from the sides. Below the top are two drawers to the front and dummy drawers on the back, all fitted with brass star handles.

The stands are ringed on the column and are strengthened by use of arched brackets, whilst the outward curving legs are fitted with brass caps and castors at the toe.

PROV: Charles Thornton of York, 1948.

# Table

**120. Table,** English, circa 1825
Mahogany; pine
H.30 (76), W.18 (46), D.16 (41)

A mahogany reading and writing table with workbox below, fitted with a pair of drawers. On top, a pair of flaps swing out to reveal a leather-covered writing surface. One flap can be elevated at different angles using a brass support rod whilst the addition of a detachable rail, makes it suitable for reading.

**121. Tripod table,** one of two, English
Mahogany. H.36 (91), W.25 (64)

The shaped hexagonal tops, richly carved on the edge,
have circular recesses intended for glasses or bowls.

    Housed within the faceted pad feet are brass and
leather castors.

PROV: The Lee family, Hartwell House, Bucks., Sotheby's, April 26,
1938, lot 263. (Described as Chocolate Tables, but their intended
purpose is still unclear).
Charles Thornton of York, 1944.

LIT: P. Macquoid & R. Edwards, *The Dictionary of English Furniture,* 1st
edn., 1924, vol.III, p.200, f.17.

NOTE: Hartwell House, a Jacobean mansion altered in 1755 by Henry
Keene for Sir William Lee, is probably best known as the home in exile
of Louis XVIII (1807-1844).

# Torchère

**122.  Torchère,** English, circa 1755
Rosewood. H.31 (58), Diam.20 (51)

A shallow tray top is supported by a turned baluster column which is carved with trailing acanthus leaves on each side of the waist. The tripod base is decorated at the knee with a central cartouche and trailing leaf, whilst the feet are fashioned in the shape of a claw.

These moveable stands, intended to support a candlestick or lamp, were meant to supplement the fixed lighting arrangements of a room.

They were normally supplied as part of a suite, standing either side of a pier table with a mirror above and usually between 3ft 6ins and 4ft 6ins in height.

PROV: Mallett, 1944.

A montage made up of sections taken from three of Chippendale's candle-stand illustrations. 3rd Edition, 1762, pl.CXLV, CXLVI, CXLVII.

**123. Torchère,** one of two, English, circa 1760 attributed to the workshop of Thomas Chippendale Mahogany. H.53 (135), W.25 (64), Top.15½ (40)

The hexagonal tops have a rising wave gallery and the triangular column is carved on the swell with scrolling leaves and trailing husks, whilst the tripod base has a scrolled cartouche and pendant leaf at the knee.

PROV: The Earl Howe, Penn House, Buckinghamshire, Christie's, Dec.8, 1933, lot 93.
Herbert Rothbarth, Esq., Christie's, May 26, 1960, lot 55.
Leidesdorf Collection, Sotheby's, June 27, 1974, lot 80.
Hotspur, 1978.

LIT: T. P. Greig, *Connoisseur*, Feb., 1934, p.131-33.
M. Harris, *Old English Furniture*, 1935, p.68.

CF.: A drawing of a stand by Chippendale, now in the Victoria and Albert Museum, London. (P. Ward-Jackson, *English Furniture Designs of the 18th Century*, 1958, f.119).

# Torchère

**124. Torchère,** English, circa 1760
Mahogany. H.39½ (100), W.18 (46)

The fretted gallery, decorated in the Gothic taste, is constructed using a laminate of mahogany and is supported by a column carved with fluting and reeding.

Three shaped legs are dovetailed into the base and are carved with a leaf pattern to knee and toe.

PROV: The Earls of Wharncliffe, Wharncliffe Hall, Wortley, Sheffield.

**125. Torchères,** English, circa 1760
Mahogany. H.36½ (63), W.20 (51)

The 'piecrust' tops are supported on columns, decorated with a pagoda top centre boss and carved lattice panels, whilst the shaped tripod bases are embellished with a hatched diamond and leaf motif.

PROV: Dr. List.
　　　Charles Thornton of York, 1946.

# Torchères

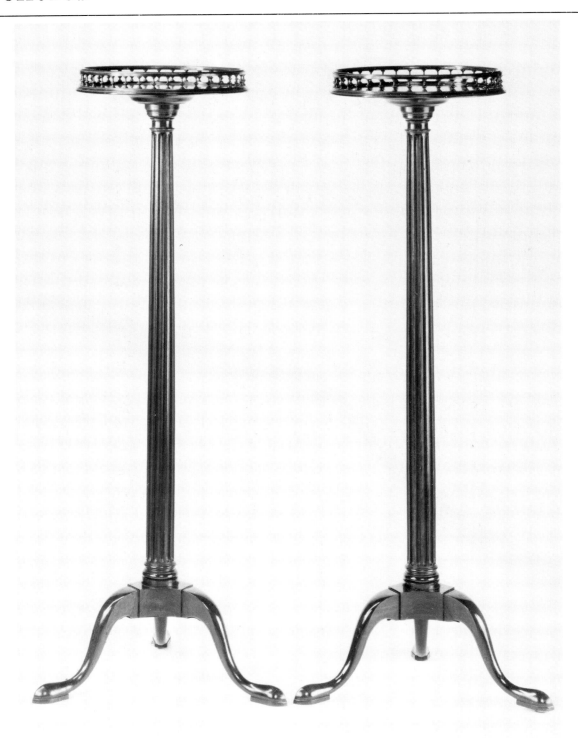

**126. Torchères,** English, circa 1765
Mahogany. H.44 (112), W.17 (43), Top.12 (30)

Circular tray tops are fitted with a spindle gallery, supported by tapering columns carved with fluting and they stand on plain tripod bases.

PROV: Mallett, 1935.

**127. Urn stand,** English, circa 1760
Mahogany; oak
H.28½ (72), W.12 (30), D.12 (30)

A fretted gallery top and teapot slide is supported on cluster column legs decorated in the Gothic taste and strengthened with pierced spandrel brackets. The feet lack their original castors.

# Miscellaneous

**128.  Panel,** English, circa 1690
Oak. L.57 (145), W.16½ (42)

A panel of flowing scrollwork with Cherubs' heads and foliage. At the centre, a gilded eagle on an anchor.

**129.  Bronze bust**
H.16 (31)
The figure is modelled on the classic marble bust of Menelaus (now in the Vatican). A King of Sparta, who, in Greek legend, was married to Helen.

**130.  Chandelier,** English, circa 1830
Bronze; glass. Diam.30 (76)
A large cut-glass dish originally fitted with an oil lamp, but now converted to electricity and having ormolu mounts chaised with foliage and 'Prince of Wales' feathers.

**131.   Music stand,** English, circa 1820
Mahogany. H.21½ (55), W.24 (61), D.16 (41)

Popularly referred to as a 'Canterbury' with spindle sides, sliding partitions and long drawers below.

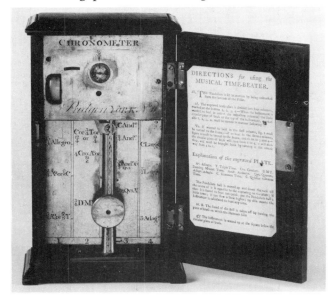

**133.   Metronome,** English, circa 1790, No. 11
William Pridgin of York (1756-1797). H.8 (20)

A clock and watchmaker, apprenticed to William Thornton, who was himself a former apprentice of Henry Hindley, the famous York clockmaker.
   Pridgin had a shop in Coney Street, York, until 1793, before moving out to Hull.

**132.   Tea-caddy,** English, circa 1790
Burr-yew; bronze. H.6 (15), W.8 (21), D.5 (13)

Shaped in the form of a sarcophagus with a locking lid that reveals two lined compartments. The edges have a delicate inlay of boxwood stringing and although the handles have been removed, the piece retains its original splayed paw feet.

**134.   Wall bracket,** English, circa 1790
Mahogany. H.12 (30), W.8 (21), D.6 (16)

A pierced fretwork gallery and scrolled supports.

# Paintings

**135. Hermel Van Steenwyck (fl.1644-58?).** A still life of dead birds and fruit on a draped table. It is painted on a wooden panel and signed. The artist was a pupil of David Bailly at Leiden in Holland and after a brief visit to the West Indies returned to Delft in 1655. 17 (43) x 22 (56)

**136. Jacob Marel (1614-85).** An overturned glass vase full of flowers with flying insects and a lizard on a stone ledge. The painting is inscribed and dated 1651 within a paper scroll. Born in Frankfurt, the artist was noted for his still life and studied under Georg Flegel and J. D. de Hean. 15 (38) x 19½ (50)

**137/138. Dirck Maas (1656-1717).** A pair of hunting scenes in wooded landscapes. The rider with the orange sash may well be William III. Maas came over to England where he painted the 'Battle of the Boyne' in celebration of the King's victory.
20½ (52) x 24 (61)

# Paintings

**139/140. Johannes Storck (fl.1660-1680).** A pair of Dutch canal scenes with rigged sailing vessels and figures amongst the terraced townhouses of Holland. Signed J. Storck, Burg. 23½ (60) x 35 (89)

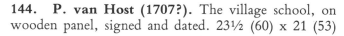

**141. School of J. Matsys (1510-1575).** The Magdalen, painted on a wooden panel. 22 (56)x17 (43)

**142. Flemish School (16th century).** St. Francis of Assisi, painted on a wooden panel. 21½ (55)x18½ (47)

**143. S. German School (16th century).** Miracle of St. Isabel, wooden panel. 27 (69) x 22 (56)

**144. P. van Host (1707?).** The village school, on wooden panel, signed and dated. 23½ (60) x 21 (53)

# Paintings

**145.   William van de Velde, the elder, (1610-1693).** The Dromedary and the United Provinces, painted engrisaille, signed and dated. 20½ (53) x 30 (76)

**146.   Abraham Storck (1630-1710).** A Dutch two-decker and other shipping offshore in a choppy sea. Signed and dated 1678. 22 (56) x 29 (74)

**147. Jonathan Richardson (1665-1745).** Portrait of the artist with his palette and manuscripts set in an oval cartouche. 6½ (17) x 5 (15)

**148. William van Mieris (1662-1747).** A portrait of a gentleman mounted in a water-gilt brass frame. EXHIB: Guildhall, London, 1895. 6¼ (16) x 4 (10)

**149. School of Frans van Mieris (1635-81).** Portrait of a gentleman dressed in black. Painted on copper and dated 1684. 22 (56) x 18 (46)

**150. Pieter van der Werff (1665-1721).** Portrait of a gentleman standing by a statue on a terrace, signed and dated 1704. 19 (48) x 15 (38)

# Paintings

**151/152. Jan Josefsz van Goyen (1596-1666).** A pair of pencil and grey wash sketches showing fisherfolk on the seashore. Initialled and dated 1634. 4½ (12) x 7½ (19)

**153/154. Jacobus Janson (1729-84).** A pair of paintings with figures outside a church, set in a wooded landscape. Both signed and dated 1765. 12 (30) x 17½ (44)

# Paintings

**155. School of Jan Evert Morel (1777-1808).** A still life of fruit and flowers set in a landscape. 19½ (50) x 23½ (60)

**156. School of H. J. Dubbels (fl1650?).** Dutch inshore boats moored to a jetty. 12 (30) x 14½ (37)

# Paintings

**157. Pieter van Slingelandt (1640-1691).** An interior view with a man and woman seated in front of a chair which supports a fiddle. Born at Leiden in Holland, the artist trained under Gerard Dou and followed the style of his master throughout his life. 16 (40) x 13 (33)

**158. Thomas Wyck (1616-1677).** Figures in the courtyard of a house, painted on a wooden panel. A Dutch artist who, having lived and worked in Italy came with his son to England at the time of the Restoration and found employment amongst the nobility, providing paintings for, amongst others, Knole, Hatfield and Ham House. 17 (43) x 14 (36)

**159. John Wilson Carmichael (1800-1868).** Shipping offshore in a stormy sea, dated 1845. The artist was born in Newcastle, where he lived and worked painting shipping scenes until 1845 when he moved to London. 27 (68) x 35 (89)

**160. Manner of D. Teniers, the Younger (1610-94).** A village scene with peasants merrymaking outside an inn. The painting bears a signature. 22 (50) x 40 (102)

# Paintings

**161.** Study of a woman with two doves.
29½ (75) x 24 (61)

**William Etty**, R.A. (1787-1849). Born in York and apprenticed to a letterpress printer in Hull. He had completed his indentures by 1806 and was then invited by his uncle to reside in London. In 1808 he became a pupil of Sir Thomas Lawrence and also put in a regular attendance at life school classes at the Royal Academy.

It was some time before his work was accepted at the Academy and it was not until 1828 that he was elected a full Academician. It was suggested by his peers that it was not befitting the dignity of his membership for him to continue with his life classes mixing with the students, but Etty said that he would rather decline the honour of membership than forego his studies.

Ill health forced him to return to York where he died in November 1849.

**162.** Nude woman, full length, holding red drapery.
25½ (65) x 20 (50)

# Paintings

**163.** Back view of a nude woman, full length. 23 (58) x 16 (41)

**164.** Figure of a seated man, painted on a panel. 19 (48) x 15½ (39)

**165.** Woodland nymphs in an Arcadian landscape. 15½ (40) x 20 (50)
EXHIB: York Art Gallery, *Pictures of the late William Etty, R.A.,* 1910.

# Porcelain

Delft large blue and white vase, the oviform body has a tall octagonal neck with a compressed spherical shaped top, painted with chinoiserie figures and other motifs - early 18th century, VE monogram, probably for Lambertus van Eenhoorn.

A famille verte biscuit figure of a carp leaping from waves (repaired) - Kangxi, 6½ins wide.

A pair of famille verte biscuit brushwashers modelled as lotus leaves, decorated with crustacea in relief (chipped) - 18th century, 5ins wide.

A pair of famille verte yellow-ground bowls incised with flowers and foliage (cracked and chipped) - square seal marks, Kangxi, 7½ins D.

A famille verte plate painted with two ladies within panels at the border - Kangxi, 9½ins D.

A famille verte dish painted with figures in a pagoda - Chenghua mark, Kangxi, 10½ins D.

A famille verte deep dish painted with panels of emblems at the border, enclosing two figures on a bridge at the centre - Kangxi, 11ins D.

A pair of famille verte ribbed saucer-dishes painted with flowers, a pheasant and foliage (cracked and chipped) - Kangxi, 10½ins D.

A famille verte dish painted with insects on foliage and flowers - Chenghua mark, Kangxi, 9ins D.

A famille verte oviform jar with an Emile Samson replacement cover, painted with panels showing Buddhistic lions, vases and vessels (damaged) - the jar Kangxi, 14ins high.

A pair of famille verte figures of standing boys holding vases in their opposite hands (one repaired) - Kangxi, 11ins high. *(top illustration)*.

A pair of famille verte dishes painted with yellow deer below pine and storks at the borders - Kangxi, 15¼ins D. *(bottom illustration)*.

A famille verte dish painted with foliage and insects (repaired) - hua mark, Kangxi, 8ins D.

A famille rose eggshell plate painted with a lady and gentleman and two children, the grey diaper-pattern border with flowers and insects (cracked) - Yongzheng, 8¼ins D.

A famille rose plate painted with figures in a scroll-shaped panel - Quianlong, 9ins D.

A famille verte dish with dragons pursuing flaming pearls-Chenghua mark, Kangxi, 11ins D.

A famille verte saucer dish painted with flowers and foliage issuing from an iron-red lozenge at the centre (chipped) - Kangxi, 7ins D.

A famille verte dish painted with chrysanthemum within six fan-shaped panels at the well (repaired) leaf mark - Kangxi, 10½ins D.

## 166. Kashan, 84 (213) x 55 (140)

A silk embossed prayer rug, circa 1910-20, from the Kashan region of Persia (now Iran).

This example has a baluster vase and bouquet of flowers within the field, which is surmounted by a flowering tree of life, a deeply religious symbol signifying immortality in the after-life and divine power. Flanking these are various flowering bushes with deer cavorting about the base and numerous birds perched amongst the foliage. The predominant bird represented in this rug is the Hoopoe, a native of Europe and the Middle East which is said to have been endowed by Allah with a gold crest. This was later converted into feathers, in answer to the petition of the persecuted wearer.

The border is filled with flowering plants and is separated from the field by indigo and sea-green stripes.

## 167. Koum Ka Pour, 80 (203) x 53 (135)

A silk and metal thread prayer rug, circa 1900, woven in a Turkish suburb of Istanbul under Royal patronage, at the workshops of the master Turkish weaver Kanata. The name Koum Ka Pour means 'gates to the sands' and this type of rug was only woven for a period of about twenty years between 1890 and 1910.

The rug is dominated by a central blood red Mihrab, (prayer niche) a common feature on prayer rugs and said to represent the alcove of the great Mosque at Mecca at which the devotee will point.

Surrounding the waisted top is a cartouche displaying Turkish poems and prayers, whilst within the elaborate border are further prayer pendants and seals.

It is most unusual to find any living creatures woven into the designs of antique Turkish rugs. Whilst the Koran does not specifically forbid these representations, most orthodox Mohammedans hold against such uses in works of art.

# Rugs

**168. Isfahan,** 81 (206) x 48 (122)

A silk pictorial rug with an ivory coloured field filled with trees, flowering plants and various animals in a similar manner to a hunting carpet, but without the human figures. Amongst the animals represented are leopards, deer, dogs, doves, roosters and peacocks, all hidden amongst the foliage.

In the pale raspberry-coloured border a simplified Herati motif of palmettes and flowering vine is used with sky blue and gold stripes at the edge.

The Herati border has its origins in the town of Herat, now situated in Afghanistan (it had been part of Persia until the 18th century) and the motif usually consists of a small rosette which sprouts lancet shaped leaves and flowering scrollwork.

Isfahan, the old capital of Persia (now Iran) was overrun by Afghan tribesmen in 1722 and no carpets were made for export again until this century.

**169. Kashan,** 82 (208) x 53 (135)

A Kashan prayer rug, circa 1910-20, with a tan field displaying a central blood red baluster vase and bouquet of flowers, flanked by flowering trees.

Peacocks and doves perch amongst the branches, whilst deer attend at the base and are joined by fish shown on the base of the vase.

The use of colours in Persian and Turkish rugs is equally symbolic in its selection as are the choice and arrangement of the motifs.

White or ivory is an almost universal symbol of death or peace, with authority usually represented by such colours as gold, yellow and purple. Sky blue, being the national colour of Persia, can also be used to denote peace, whilst red symbolises joy, life and all the goodly virtues. Indigo blue signifies solitude, pink, the application of divine wisdom and green a colour sacred to Mohammedans.

## 170. Kashan, 78 (198) x 52 (132)

A Kashan prayer rug, circa 1920-30, with an indigo coloured field, decorated with a flowering tree of life. Perched amongst the branches are various birds and animals, with leaping deer and feeding ducks at the base. The symbolism intended by the use of various creatures can be quite confusing and with many representations, the meaning for the Hindus may well be the exact opposite of that intended by Mohammedans. Some of the least contentious are: the dove, a universal symbol of peace; the peacock denoting beauty; the dog, a talisman against robbers, spells and diseases; the duck, a symbol of a happy and faithful marriage; and the stork, a symbol of dishonesty to the Indians but a symbol of longevity to the Chinese.

## 171. Tehran, 77 (196) x 53 (135)

An early 20th century cotton rug, probably woven in the Tehran or central region of Persia (Iran) and displaying some strong western influences, especially in the choice of colours and in the design.

The central tree of life is flanked, symmetrically, by two flowering trees and birds, snakes and plants are arranged in similar formation.

### List of Remaining

Other carpets in the collection include various early 20th century Tekke Turkomans, one with the unusual feature of two human faces woven into the border and a Yomud Hatchlie (prayer rug) all from the Turkestan region of the U.S.S.R.

Also featured is a Hamadan runner with brown field and blue floral border, plus a Serapi runner, both from the western reaches of Persia (Iran).

# Silver

**172.** A Charles II two handled cup and cover with tapering sides and a flat stepped cover. The plain raised body has a slightly everted rim and has plain cast G-shaped handles. The side has been engraved with a scrolled mantle of reeds which enclose a coat of arms. Stamped on the lid and base the maker's marks consist of the letters IN within a heart. H.7½ (19), W.9 (23)

**173.** A William and Mary mug with a reeded scroll handle and cylindrical neck. The bulbous sided base is decorated in the chinoiserie taste with pheasants and foliage and has the London mark for 1689 together with the makers mark TC. H.4 (10)

**174.** A William III circular salver on a cylindrical spreading stem and having chased gadrooned rims. The centre has been engraved with a circular scrolling cartouche containing an eagle's claw crest and is assayed with the London hallmark, circa 1700, by Joseph Ward. Diam.9¼ (34)

**175.** A George III brandy saucepan of baluster shape with a double-domed cover and having a wooden finial. The sides and lid are engraved with a crest and the initials E.D. and the piece was made in York 1802 by the firm of Hampston, Prince and Cattle. Diam.3½ (9)

# Silver

**176.** A two-handled Commonwealth cup of slightly flared form. The cast S-scroll handles are decorated with human masks and foliage matted to pick out the decoration. On the base are further chased flowerheads, together with the London marks for 1674 and the maker's mark HN, set within a shield. W.7 (18)

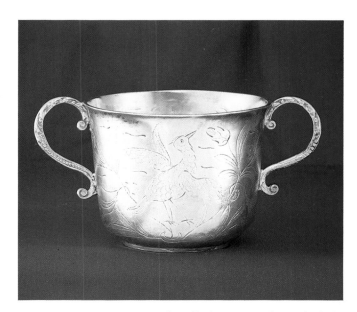

**177.** A James II two-handled cup with a slightly everted rim and cast S-scroll handles decorated with leaf and beading. The sides are engraved in chinoiserie fashion with pheasants seen amongst foliage and the interior is gilded. By Marmaduke Best, York, circa 1685. W.6½ (17)

York was an important centre for the production of items made in silver and gold and was in fact the first of the seven provincial cities to be given its own charter and guild mark.

From the late 15th century through to 1699, the city adopted the device of a half-crowned leopard's head and a half Fleur-de-Lys divided per 'pale' in a circle (the emblem now used by the York Civic Trust), and from 1700 onwards, this changed to the five lions of England upon the Cross of St. George. By about 1720 however, there was a severe decline in work for the assay office, thus causing it to close.

The York silversmiths had then to pass their work through the other assay offices and it resulted in many of the smiths leaving York to work in centres such as Newcastle and Chester.

In 1773, however, York resurrected its assay office, presumably in an effort to compete with the newly opened offices of Birmingham and Sheffield and continued to function for some 80 years before finally closing in 1857. The most famous of the York silversmiths were working during the period of the Restoration and makers such as John Plummer, Marmaduke Best, Robert Williamson and Thomas Mangay were producing some of the finest pieces that survive today.

Little information exists at the moment on the silversmiths working during the first half of the 18th century, but by the 1770's several prominent firms were operating in York, one of them being Hampston and Prince. By the end of the century, the Cattle family had joined the firm and on the retirement of John Hampston, the firm then became known as Prince and Cattle.

For further information refer to: C. N. Moore, The silver of Hampston and Prince, of York, *Antique Dealer and Collectors Guide,* August, 1986, p.48-51.

*Not shown*
**178.** A George III plain tapering cylindrical beaker with plain moulded base and engraved on the side with a rococo cartouche and the name J. F. Thiodon. The interior is gilded and the piece hallmarked with the York mark of 1791, J. Hampston and J. Prince. H.3¾ (10)

# Bibliography

1   G. Beard, 1966.
*Georgian Craftsmen and their work.*

2   G. Beard, 1981.
*Craftsmen and Interior Decoration in England, 1660-1820.*

*3   O. Brackett, 1950. *English Furniture illustrated.*

*4   Cescinsky & Webster, 1914.
*English Domestic Clocks.*

*5   H. Cescinsky & E. Gribble, 1922.
*Early English Furniture & Woodwork.*

6   T. Chippendale, 1754.
*The Gentleman & Cabinet-maker's Director,* 1st ed.

7   T. Chippendale, 1762.
*The Gentleman & Cabinet-maker's Director,* 3rd ed.

*8   A. Coleridge, 1968. *Chippendale Furniture.*

9   Dawson, Drover, Parkes, 1982.
*Early English Clocks.*

*10   R. Edwards, 1954.
*The Dictionary of English Furniture, vol. 1-3.*

*11   R. Edwards & M. Jourdain, 1955.
*Georgian Cabinet-makers.*

*12   C. Gilbert, 1978.
*The Life and Work of Thomas Chippendale.*

13   N. Goodison, 1977.
*English Barometers, 1680-1860.*

*14   E. Gorer & J. F. Blacker, 1911.
*Les Porcelaines et les Pierres Dures Chinoises, vol 1.2.*

*15   R. L. Hobson, 1915.
*Chinese Pottery & Porcelain.*

*16   R. L. Hobson, 1925.
*The later ceramic wares of China.*

*17   W. E. Hurcomb, 1929.
*The Wetherfield Collection.*

18   Ince & Mayhew, 1762.
*The Universal system of Household Furniture.
Facsimile reprint with preface by Ralph Edwards 1960.*

19   G. Jackson-Stops, 1985.
*The Treasure Houses of Britain.*

*20   M. Jourdain, 1922.
*English Decoration and Furniture 1760-1820.*

*21   M. Jourdain, 1924.
*English Decoration & Furniture in the early Renaissance*

*22   M. Jourdain & F. Rose, 1953.
*English Furniture, The Georgian Period, 1750-1830.*

*23   A. Kendrick & C. Tattersall, 1922.
*Hand woven Carpets, Oriental & European.*

*24   F. Lenygon, 1922.
*Decoration in England 1640-1760.*

*25   F. Lenygon, 1922.
*Furniture in England 1660-1760.*

26   B. Loomes, 1985.
*Grandfather clocks & their cases.*

27   B. Loomes, 1985. *Yorkshire Clockmakers.*

28   D. Marot, 1707.
*Werken van D. Marot, Groot Britanje.*

*29   P. Macquoid & R. Edwards, 1924-27.
*The Dictionary of English Furniture, vol. 1-3.*

*30   P. Macquoid, 1923.
*A History of English Furniture, vol. 1-4.*

*31   W. Menzies, 1928. *Collecting Antiques.*

32   T. Robinson, 1982. *The Longcase Clock.*

*33   C. & R. Scott, 1961.
*Antique Porcelain Digest.*

*34   T. A. Strange, 1935.
*English Furniture, Woodwork, Decoration.*

*35   R. W. Symonds, 1923.
*Old English Walnut & Lacquer Furniture.*

*36   R. W. Symonds, 1924.
*The Present State of English Furniture.*

*37   R. W. Symonds, 1929. *English Furniture.*

*38   R. W. Symonds, 1940.
*Masterpieces of English Furniture & Clocks.*

*39   C. Tattersall, 1922.
*Hand woven carpets, Oriental & European.*

40   V.A.M., 1982, Maurice Tomlin.
*Catalogue of Adam Period Furniture.*

41   V.A.M., 1984.
*Rococo - Art & Design in Hogarth's England.*

42   J. Walker, 1985.
*Hull & East Riding Clocks.*

*43   W. Watts, 1924. *Old English Silver.*

Our thanks to Dick Reid and to Potterton Books for sight of Thomas Chippendale's *Director* [6] & [7].

Items marked with an * formed part of Noel Terry's library.

Articles on the Collection:
C. Cator, *Country Life,* Sept. 5, 1985, p.654-6.
P. Brown, *Antique Collector,* June, 1986, p.90-97.

# Chronology

| Year of Purchase | Supplier | Code. No. | Item | Material | Location | Page No. |
|---|---|---|---|---|---|---|
| 1918 | V | F10 | Bureau Bookcase | Mahogany | 2nd Floor | 38 |
| 1923 | SH | P1 | Birds & Fruit by H. van Steenwyck | Oil | Dining Room | 132 |
| 1926 | A | F12 | Library Armchair | Mahogany | Drawing Room | 58 |
| 1927 | V | F4 | Japanned Cabinet | Lacquer | Dining Room | 87 |
| 1928 | T | F4 | Spinet | Mahogany/Walnut | Saloon | 99 |
| 1928 | T | F1 | Tallboy Secretaire | Mahogany | Anne's Bedroom | 82 |
| 1928 | SH | P2 | Peasants Merrymaking - D. Teniers | Oil | Dining Room | 141 |
| 1928 | SH | P3 | Hunting Parties x 2 - D. Maas | Oil | Saloon | 133 |
| 1929 | SH | P5 | Dutch Two Decker - A. Storck | Oil | Dining Room | 136 |
| 1929 | V | S3 | Small Silver Mug - W & Mary | Silver | Dining Room | 148 |
| 1930 | V | S4 | Salver - J. Ward, 1700 | Silver | Dining Room | 148 |
| 1930 | SH | P7 | Flowers & Lizard - J. Marel | Oil | Dining Room | 132 |
| 1930 | SH | P8 | Figures in a Courtyard - T. Wyck | Oil | Library | 140 |
| 1930 | SH | P9 | Figures in a Churchyard x 2 - J. Janson | Oil | Library | 138 |
| 1931 | SH | P10 | Miracle of St. Isobel - S. German School | Oil | Viscount's Bedroom | 135 |
| 1931 | SH | P11 | St. Francis of Assisi - Flemish School | Oil | Viscount's Bedroom | 135 |
| 1931 | M | F1 | Breakfront Bureau Bookcase | Mahogany | Library | 36 |
| 1931 | T | F6 | Pair of Card Tables | Mahogany | Saloon | 114 |
| 1931 | T | F6 | Stool | Walnut | Anne's Bedroom | 50 |
| 1932 | M | F2 | Longcase Clock - Anderson of Liverpool | Mahogany | Hall | 24 |
| 1932 | SH | P13 | Gentleman - Van der Werff | Oil | Library | 137 |
| 1932 | SH | P14 | Self Portrait - J. Richardson | Oil | Library | 137 |
| 1932 | SH | P15 | Village School - P. van Host | Oil | Dining Room | 135 |
| 1932 | M | F5 | Chest of Drawers | Mahogany | Hall | 74 |
| 1932 | M | F31 | Tripod Table | Mahogany | Library | 109 |
| 1933 | M | F4 | Gateleg Table | Walnut | Drawing Room | 100 |
| 1934 | SH | P19 | The Magdalen - a. J. Matsys | Oil | Viscount's Bedroom | 135 |
| 1934 | SH | P20 | Canal Scenes x 2 - J. Storck | Oil | Hall | 134 |
| 1934 | M | F8 | Bureau - sloping front | Walnut | Hall | 32 |
| 1934 | M | F7 | Commode | Mahogany | 2nd Floor | 72 |
| 1934 | M | F11 | Commode | Mahogany | Hall | 84 |
| 1934 | M | F12 | Pair of Chairs - W. & M. | Walnut | Hall | 46 |
| 1934 | M | F13 | Canterbury | Mahogany | Library | 131 |
| 1934 | M | F14 | Artist's Table | Mahogany | Library | 103 |
| 1935 | M | F17 | Longcase Clock - D. Quare | Walnut | Drawing Room | 19 |
| 1935 | T | F11 | Silver Table | Mahogany | 2nd Floor | 112 |
| 1935 | M | F20 | Chest of Drawers | Mahogany | 2nd Floor | 85 |
| 1935 | M | F19 | Centre Table - Salver top | Mahogany | Saloon | 105 |
| 1935 | M | F16 | Torchères - Fluted pillars | Mahogany | Dining Room | 128 |
| 1935 | M | F1 | Double Dome Cabinet | Walnut | Drawing Room | 31 |
| 1935 | M | F1 | Parquetry Cabinet | Walnut & Kingwood | Drawing Room | 39 |
| 1935 | M | F25 | Bronze Cistern | Bronze/Mahogany | Library | 88 |
| 1936 | M | F24 | Single Chair x 3 | Mahogany | Saloon | 63 |
| 1936 | T | F12 | Settee | Mahogany | Saloon | 67 |
| 1937 | M | F22 | Single Chair | Walnut | Hall | 47 |
| 1937 | M | F23 | Seaweed Marquetry Cabinet | Walnut | Drawing Room | 40 |
| 1937 | M | S12 | Two handled Cup - M. Best, York 1685 | Silver | Dining Room | 149 |
| 1937 | T | F13 | Torchère - hexagonal top | Mahogany | Drawing Room | 126 |
| 1937 | M | F27 | Single Chair x 2 | Mahogany | Drawing Room | 61 |
| 1937 | M | F28 | Ladderback Chair x 8 & one Carver | Mahogany | Dining Room | 62 |
| 1937 | M | F26 | Bracket Clock - D. Quare | Marquetry case | Viscount's Bedroom | 20 |
| 1937 | SH | P24 | Gentleman - W. van Mieris | Oil on copper | Library | 137 |
| 1937 | SH | P25 | The Dromedary - W. van de Velde | Oil | Dining Room | 136 |
| 1938 | SH | P21 | Fisherfolk x 2 - Van Goyen | Pencil | Bedroom Stairs | 138 |
| 1938 | SH | P22 | Lady & Parrot - G. Cocques | Oil | Library | N.S. |
| 1938 | SH | P23 | Dutch Shipping - S of H. J. Dubbels | Oil | Library | 139 |
| 1938 | T | F15 | Winged Armchair | Mahogany | Library | 54 |
| 1938 | M | F29 | Buffet | Oak | Hall | 30 |
| 1938 | T | F17 | Plate Buckets | Mahogany | Dining Room | 94 |
| 1938 | T | F14 | Urn Stand | Mahogany | Saloon | 129 |
| 1938 | T | F16 | Dressing Glass | Walnut | Annes Bedroom | 90 |
| 1939 | T | F18 | Gainsborough Armchair | Mahogany | Saloon | 60 |
| 1941 | T | — | Longcase Regulator - J. Boynton | Mahogany | Hall | 25 |
| 1941 | T | F21 | Cabinet on Stand | Mahogany | 2nd Floor | 45 |
| 1942 | V | F2 | Wheel Barometer - G. Hallifax | Walnut | Hall | 10 |
| 1944 | M | F31 | Pier Glass | Gesso | Drawing Room | 93 |
| 1944 | M | F30 | Torchère | Rosewood | Drawing Room | 124 |
| 1944 | T | F22 | Drinks Table x 2 | Mahogany | Saloon | 123 |

151

# Chronology

| Year of Purchase | Supplier | Code. No. | Item | Material | Location | Page No. |
|---|---|---|---|---|---|---|
| 1944 | M | S18 | Two handled Cup - H.N., 1674 | Silver | Dining Room | 149 |
| 1945 | T | F23 | Stick Barometer - J. Agar, York | Mahogany | Hall | 11 |
| 1945 | T | F24 | Stool - needlework seat | Walnut | Viscount's Bedroom | 48 |
| 1945 | M | F32 | Commode | Mahogany | Saloon | 83 |
| 1945 | M | F33 | Commode | Mahogany | Saloon | 73 |
| 1945 | M | F34 | Wing Armchair | Mahogany | Drawing Room | 52 |
| 1945 | M | F35 | Bedside Cupboard | Mahogany | Anne's Bedroom | 89 |
| 1945 | M | F36 | Armchair x 3 | Mahogany | Grand Stairs | 55 |
| 1946 | M | F37 | Bracket Clock - Tompion & Banger | Ebony case | Saloon | 22 |
| 1946 | ST | F4 | Torchère x 2 | Mahogany | Drawing Room | 127 |
| 1946 | T | F26 | Kneehole Dressing Table | Mahogany | Anne's Bedroom | 111 |
| 1946 | T | F27 | Bureau Bookcase | Mahogany | Shop | 37 |
| 1947 | T | F30 | Longcase clock - T. Tompion | Walnut case | Library | 18 |
| 1947 | T | F31 | Chest of Drawers | Mahogany | 2nd Floor | 75 |
| 1947 | T | F32 | Games Table | Sabacu | Drawing Room | 118 |
| 1947 | T | F29 | Breakfront Bureau Bookcase | Mahogany | Library | 35 |
| 1947 | T | F29 | Sideboard | Mahogany | Dining Room | 98 |
| 1947 | M | F39 | Longcase Clock - E. East | Walnut | Dining Room | 15 |
| 1947 | M | F40 | Secretaire Cabinet | Mahogany | Dining Room | 44 |
| 1947 | M | F40 | Single Chair x 4 | Mahogany | Dining Room | 56 |
| 1947 | M | F38 | Cabinet on stand | Walnut | Drawing Room | 41 |
| 1947 | M | F41 | Bombé Chest | Mahogany | Saloon | 79 |
| 1947 | T | F42 | Dressing Bureau | Walnut | Viscount's Bedroom | 33 |
| 1948 | M | F43 | Ivory Stick Barometer - D. Quare | Ivory column | Hall | 9 |
| 1948 | T | F34 | Bellows | Walnut | Library | 13 |
| 1949 | M | F45 | Longcase Clock - Windmills | Marquetry case | Saloon | 21 |
| 1949 | M | F44 | Armchair x 2 - J. Gordon | Mahogany | Saloon | 59 |
| 1949 | M | F46 | Commode | Mahogany | Saloon | 76 |
| 1949 | M | F47 | Kneehole Side Table | Walnut | Hall | 101 |
| 1950 | — | — | Stick Barometer - Polti | Mahogany | Hall | 12 |
| 1950 | M | F48 | Armchair | Walnut | Library | 51 |
| 1950 | M | F49 | Dressing Bureau | Mahogany | Anne's Bedroom | 34 |
| 1950 | M | F50 | Armchair - shield back | Mahogany | Drawing Room | 68 |
| 1950 | M | F51 | Kneehole Table - Gothic taste | Mahogany | Library | 107 |
| 1951 | M | F52 | Bachelor's Chest | Walnut | Viscount's Bedroom | 70 |
| 1951 | M | F53 | Tripod Table | Mahogany | Dining Room | 104 |
| 1952 | V | F1 | Bracket Clock - E. East | Ebony case | Hall | 14 |
| 1952 | M | F54 | Single Chair x 2 | Walnut | Library | 53 |
| 1954 | H | F1 | Dumb-Waiter | Mahogany | Dining Room | 108 |
| 1954 | M | F10 | Quartetto Tables | Amboyna | Drawing Room | 117 |
| 1963 | H | F2 | Secretaire Cabinet | Mahogany | Anne's Bedroom | 95 |
| 1964 | M | F3 | Secretaire Cabinet - W. Vile | Mahogany | Viscount's Bedroom | 96 |
| 1964 | T | F35 | Longcase Clock - H. Jones | Walnut case | Grand Stairs | 17 |
| 1967 | T | F36 | Reading and Writing Table | Mahogany | Viscount's Bedroom | 123 |
| 1970 | — | F10 | Bracket Clock - J. Knibb | Ebony case | Anne's Bedroom | 16 |
| 1973 | V | F11 | Bracket Clock - G. Graham | Ebony case | Drawing Room | 23 |
| 1974 | H | F4 | Centre Table | Mahogany | Saloon | 110 |
| 1975 | H | F5 | Gainsborough Armchair | Mahogany | Saloon | 57 |
| 1975 | H | F6 | Side Chair x 4 | Walnut | Viscount's Bedroom | 49 |
| 1976 | H | F7 | Dressing Commode | Mahogany | Anne's Bedroom | 81 |
| 1976 | H | F8 | Card Table | Mahogany | Drawing Room | 115 |
| 1977 | H | F3 | Clothes Press | Mahogany | Viscounts Bedroom | 71 |
| 1977 | H | F10 | Dressing Cabinet | Mahogany | Dining Room | 43 |
| 1978 | H | F11 | Torchères | Mahogany | Dining Room | 125 |

Some of the paintings (including all by William Etty) carpets and porcelain are not recorded or coded and their origins are as yet, unclear.

Suppliers: T — Charles Thornton, York. M — Mallett. H — Hotspur. SH — Sheridan.